The Platform Ticket

Memories and Musings of
a Hospice]

The Platform Ticket

Memories and Musings of a Hospice Doctor

Derek Doyle

The Pentland Press Limited
Edinburgh • Cambridge • Durham • USA

© Derek Doyle 1999

First published in 1999 by
The Pentland Press Ltd.
1 Hutton Close
South Church
Bishop Auckland
Durham

British Library Cataloguing in Publication Data.
A Catalogue record for this book is available
from the British Library.

ISBN 1 85821 725 3

Typeset by CBS, Martlesham Heath, Ipswich, Suffolk
Printed and bound by Antony Rowe Ltd., Chippenham

'To every thing there is a season, and a time to every purpose
  under the heaven:
A time to be born and a time to die;
A time to plant and a time to pluck up that which is planted;
A time to kill and a time to heal; a time to break down and a
  time to build up;
A time to weep and a time to laugh; a time to mourn and a time
  to dance;
A time to cast away stones, and a time to gather stones together;
A time to embrace, and a time to refrain from embracing;
A time to eat and a time to lose; a time to keep and a time to cast
  away;
A time to rend and a time to sew; a time to keep silence and a
  time to speak;
A time to love and a time to hate; a time of war and a time of
  peace.'

Ecclesiastes 3: 1-8

To my patients who shared with me
more than I ever gave to them.

Contents

Foreword

by Dr Josephina Magno, MD

Founder/President Emeritus of the International Hospice
Institute and College

Early in the mid 1970s when the concept of hospice/palliative care
was just beginning in the United States the biggest problem that
emerged was the indifference of the medical profession towards
hospice care. A Task Force created by the International Hospice
Institute (IHI) to explain this phenomenon submitted a report which
said that the reason for this attitude of physicians towards terminal
care was 'a lack of understanding by most physicians of what the
concept of hospice/palliative care was.' The recommendation was
to provide training on hospice care specifically for physicians.

Even in these early days, several known authorities on hospice
care suggested to me that one way to solve the problem was to ask
Dr Derek Doyle to come to the United States to teach our doctors.
It took almost four years before I finally succeeded in getting him
to come to the IHI Symposium to be part of the faculty. That first
visit started a friendship of many years during which I have followed
his career with admiration and awe. The man never stops. He is all
over the world giving lectures and conducting workshops for
professionals and non-professionals on how to provide hospice/
palliative care. In his spare time, he has also written many books
and countless scientific publications which are veritable treasuries
of knowledge for generations of hospice care givers yet to come.

This book, The Platform Ticket: Memories and Musings of a

Hospice Doctor, is different, because it does not set out to lecture or instruct the reader. However, I have found it one of the most useful teachings on how to provide hospice/palliative care I have ever read because it talks about real life patients: what they said, what he said, how he reacted and so forth. The stories are real, the people are real. Many of them are poignant and deeply moving but some are humorous and others sad. Through them all Dr Doyle uses the word 'humbling' and speaks of how his patients have taught him so much, not only about dying but also about living and about life itself.

I would recommend this book as prescribed reading for all who are already involved in hospice/palliative care, and for those medical and nursing students who are contemplating a career in this field, and for anyone who wants to know more about such care. Apart from the stories, the book discusses serious issues in terminal care including euthanasia and physician assisted suicide, from the perspective of both the patients and the carers. It also examines the various ways in which hospice/palliative care can best be provided.

I feel so much wiser from having read this book, not least because of Dr Doyle's style of writing. It is so elegant, picturesque and often extremely funny. We are blessed for his sharing with us his 'memories and musings as a hospice doctor for 20 years.'

Josephina Magno, MD

Chapter I

Introduction

'A time to keep silence and a time to speak.'

Most of us are familiar with the experience. We are on a flight and have said little to the stranger beside us beyond the usual pleasantries or perhaps a few critical comments on the weather, air traffic control, the baggage handlers or the country's economic situation. We have had all we want of the meal offered to us and, our tongues loosened by that glass of wine, we turn to each other and start up a conversation.

Most people enjoy this time-filler but doctors dread that question everyone asks – 'What line of business are you in?' If they are foolish and admit to being a doctor almost invariably the conversation changes immediately to the recent experiences of the fellow traveller and at least ten members of his family. The doctor scarcely has time to finish his coffee before he is being told of colourful features of the rare diseases his family seems prone to or their doctors' inability to diagnose these variants of what anyone could recognize as bubonic plague.

The doctor is fortunate if he gets off so lightly, only having to spend the rest of the flight *listening* to this saga, unless of course his flight is to Australia, in which case he makes arrangements to stop over in Singapore (only to find that his companion in the next flight also has a fascinating medical history. In time he learns that everyone has a fascinating medical history if they are sitting next to a doctor.). All too often a shirt or blouse is furtively pulled up to

1

reveal an operation scar. Its owner's eyes fix on you as if to ask 'ever seen one as big as that?' Sometimes it is not just a look. The owner of a scar usually enjoys developing the conversation at this point. 'Impressive, eh? Well, as they say, every scar tells a tale and believe me this one has quite a tale to tell. Want to hear it?' He does not wait for an answer. For him this is curtain call.

The experienced medical traveller knows that anything he says will never be adequate. What is called for is a very long in-drawing of breath as the eyes open wider and wider, ever so slowly moving away from the scar and its owner to the distant cabin window. Eyebrows still raised he must then give a long low whistle. That usually works and the doctor can be sure that for the next few months the scar's proud owner will dine out on what a famous doctor said to him on a recent flight.

Such encounters, whether in planes or at parties, bring out the worst in some doctors. I know one, a specialist in infectious diseases, who never admits to being a doctor. When asked what 'line of business' he is in he usually looks straight ahead and in a conspiratorial whisper says 'biological warfare'. He assures me no one has ever asked any more questions but he has, on several occasions, been embarrassed when the enquirer asked to be moved to another seat on the plane. Another colleague elects to tell the whole truth, in a voice which ensures he is heard – 'I'm a doctor who treats AIDS in sexual deviants.' He swears by that conversation stopper. Another, an orthopaedic surgeon, says he believes in being totally honest. He just says he is a successful mechanic! Another, equally honest, always tells the inquisitive fellow traveller that he is in the plumbing business but does not go on to explain that he is a urological surgeon. He has obviously had someone show him more than his scar and learned his lesson.

Personally I have never managed to get away with anything but the truth. I used just to mutter that I was a 'sort of doctor' but immediately the questioner homes in to see whether you are a good catch (after all you are only over Germany and Sydney is several hours away) and asks where is your general practice. You try not to appear too superior but feel you have to tell him you are actually a hospital specialist. But this only leads to an apology that you had not been recognized as being so elevated, and the inevitable question 'which speciality?' There is no escape. How far is it to Sydney?

'Well, I'm retired now but I used to work as a doctor in a hospice, so my speciality is palliative medicine.' The effect of those few words is quite dramatic. It could not be any more dramatic if the pilot was to come on the plane's PA system and say he was about to make an emergency landing. The man or woman in the seat beside you fixes their gaze on you and utters a long 'Reeeeeeally! Oh how very interesting.' The next few hours are filled with minute by minute, blow by blow accounts of the deaths of all known relatives, verbatim reports on every significant conversation, interrupted only occasionally by a sideways look to ensure that the doctor is still awake and listening in rapt fascination.

Just occasionally, however, someone says 'Goodness, how fascinating! Do tell me more about it. What's it like in a hospice? I've always wanted to know but never met someone like you who could tell me.' There then follows an embarrassed joke 'after all no-one ever comes back to tell us about the hospice, do they?' and then they think better of it when they sense that I have probably heard that one before.

'What's it like in a hospice?' 'What do you get out of working there?' 'Does it affect you in any way, does it change you, if you know what I mean? I imagine it is terribly depressing work.'

This little book is my answer to those questions. 'What's it like in a hospice? Does it affect you in any way? How does it alter you? Have *you* changed, if you don't mind me asking?'

My interest in how you describe a hospice and what it 'does' for patients and carers alike was kindled many years ago when a hospice nurse conducted a small survey of her patients and their relatives, asking them the question, 'What words would you use to describe the hospice and how you feel here?' I suppose she expected descriptions like 'sad, frightening, tragic, terrifying, gloomy, miserable,' for how else do we all feel about death, particularly when it is our own. Wasn't it Woody Allen who said he was not frightened of dying so long as he wasn't there when it happened?

To everyone's surprise by far the commonest word in response to the nurse's questions was 'safe' – surely the last word one would expect when you recall that all the patients under care have advanced disease and are likely to die within the next few months, a few much sooner. Some suggested words like 'dignified', 'respected' 'valued' 'incredible' while others offered phrases like 'the happiest place I've ever been in' or 'like a hotel where they can never do enough for you' or 'the most amazing experience of my life' or 'the only place where I have ever felt wanted or valued'. To me the most surprising comment was '. . . in here I've enjoyed the happiest days of my life.' Am I alone in finding this truly remarkable? I suspect not.

It must not be thought that the people taking part in her survey were blind to why they were there. None of them was euphoric or living in a fantasy world. What was so remarkable about their descriptive words was that they chose them knowing how short was their life. They were not under the influence of drugs or drink. They knew they were dying and had known for a very long time. They chose them as a result of what they had so recently gone through and what they were now experiencing. Most of them offered words like 'safe' and immediately went on to explain what they meant or qualified it with their reasons for saying so.

'I feel people have not been completely honest with me for the last few years and, of course, I can understand why. I'm not blaming them. It's just that when you are as ill as I am you want the truth and not a lot of white lies, well-intentioned as they may be. Here I sense that they will always be honest and open with me. That's what makes me feel safe.'

'Here the nurses and the doctors presumably know my background and what a miserable so-and-so I've been but still they can't do enough for me. I feel accepted. It's a curious feeling. I feel I don't need to pretend I am what I am not, if you know what I mean.'

'Here they seem to know you're anxious or even terrified out of your mind or have some special problem even before you mention it and you feel it's OK to talk about it. You'll never be told to "snap out of it" or "pull yourself together".'

'I know very well how busy the nurses and doctors are – you'd be blind if you didn't see the hours they work here – but they all seem to have time to listen to you when you need them, and every little thing seems to matter to them.'

Close on twenty years working as a doctor in a large hospice taught me more than I could ever describe. My principal teachers were, of course, the patients themselves; a few rich and many poor, several frightened and many brave, a few articulate enough to be able to explain all they felt but most just lost for words but still able to take your hand and enjoy silent companionship. All, save a tiny handful, deeply affected by their experiences and, as they themselves would admit, irrevocably changed.

It was Dr Samuel Johnson who wrote '. . . when a man knows he is to be hanged in a fortnight, it concentrates his mind wonderfully.' Those of us privileged to have worked in a hospice, whilst most certainly not suggesting that our patients feel as though they are inmates on 'Death Row', have watched in amazement as personalities have blossomed, friendships been sealed and life, for some, taken on a new meaning. As I hope to illustrate in this book, time in a hospice is not usually spent 'waiting for the end' or counting down the final hours but, hackneyed as it may sound, in living rather than in dying. For many people – patients, loved ones and professionals – it is a time of self-discovery, of reflection and often of change. For some it is indeed the first time they have felt valued, or needed, or even useful. For others it is the first time they have asked the questions that Man must always have asked – why must he suffer, does suffering ever have any meaning, what is life all about, is there a God, does life have any meaning ?

What is so interesting for me, a doctor, is not just what my patients experienced and shared with me but what I, and many of my professional colleagues in this work, also experienced, and how we changed as a result of our work. How could it be otherwise when you saw someone with a reputation for selfishness turn into someone characterized by thoughtfulness and consideration for others; when you saw someone paralysed by fear relaxing before your eyes when their every question was answered truthfully; when you watched a young mother breast feed her baby as the other three children played on Daddy's bed just days before he died. Who could not be moved by such a scene and not ask 'why'? What is happening here? What is the secret of this place? Who would ever expect to hear such good jokes as are exchanged in a hospice?

Perhaps I never discovered the 'secret' or will be unable to describe it for readers but it was there all the same. Time without number a family doctor would phone and ask for one of his patients to be admitted to bring unbearable pain under control. He would list everything he had tried and describe the most agonizing experiences of the patient. You felt for him and his overwhelming sense of failure or inadequacy. You asked the nurses to inform you as soon as the patient was brought in by the ambulancemen, fully expecting to hear the screams and see the tears. The scene which met you was quite the opposite. There was the patient sitting up in bed looking remarkably happy and certainly not in agony. What had happened? 'I've always dreaded having to come in here, doctor, but now that I'm here I feel so much more comfortable. It's a silly thing to say, I suppose, but I feel less pain already. I feel safe.' That before he had even been examined and new treatment started.'

For those who perhaps know less than others of us about hospices a few words of explanation might help. Using the same word that was used in the Middle Ages when hospices were to be found across Europe, offering places of rest, refreshment and care, for travellers and Crusaders, a handful were started in France, Ireland and England in the first half of the twentieth century, no longer for travellers but for the terminally ill, travellers only in the sense that they are on that road which links this life and the next.

Since the late 1960s, inspired by the example of St Christopher's Hospice in London, many have been established in the United Kingdom, North America and, more recently in more than fifty countries worldwide. As the millennium approaches there are more than 6,000 hospice programmes with more being added every week. We must be careful to describe them as 'hospice programmes' or 'hospice services' or more correctly as 'palliative care services' rather than merely 'hospice'.

Most offer comprehensive care, seeing people in their own homes as well as offering residential care when for some reason they cannot be looked after at home; many also have Day Hospices for those still at home but able to visit the unit during the day; yet other services care for people in general and specialist hospitals.

Gone are the days when everyone had to have cancer to qualify for hospice care. Gone are the days when someone going into a hospice never came out. Today hospice services care for people with a range of mortal illnesses, cancer certainly the principal one. They go in and out, often many times, to have their pain relieved, to have help with their sickness or their frailty, or sometimes just for a break for them and their families. They know, their doctors know, their families all know, that there are no cures but there are many, many things which can be done to relieve unnecessary suffering. The word for that is 'palliation', hence the correct description of this work being 'palliative care' and the professional title for many hospice doctors being 'consultant in palliative medicine.' Hospice care and palliative care are, essentially, one and the same thing. It is, more than anything else, a philosophy of care; a philosophy which can be practised in a new or an old building, in patients' homes, and in general and specialist hospitals all over the country.

One word used by doctors and nurses to describe their work, but a word not likely ever to be used by the patients, though they benefit from it, is 'holistic'. It is easy enough to explain that that means 'whole person care', but does that make us any the wiser? Most doctors would claim, often with good reason, that they are concerned with the whole person, rather than just with his or her appendix, for example. The fact remains that modern medicine has tended to focus on some part of the body which needs a repair job doing on it. Holistic care sees the patient as a person, as a whole being and sets out to respect not only the person's body but also his mind, his soul and the social circle in which he functions and contributes.

This principle, this concept, is often expressed somewhat crudely, but nevertheless accurately, as caring for the person rather than a part of the person which is malfunctioning. Hospice care, or palliative care as we should call it, focuses not on the man's cancer but on the man with the cancer, and his physical, emotional, social and spiritual needs, as they are all affected by his cancer.

There is no mystery about all this, no new breakthrough or discovery. It is what we all want when we are unwell, and what we desperately need when we are mortally ill. There comes a time when we hardly care whether or not the doctors can do any more for the cancer but we hope and pray they can, and will, do everything possible for the pain it is producing. We need to know that they will recognize how frightened we are, confronted by an experience we have never faced before in our lives.

Family doctors would claim that holistic 'whole person care' is what general practice is all about and I believe that is true. Call it 'old-fashioned, bedside medicine' if you like. It is what we all want but sometimes do not get. There is no denying that in many hospitals the complex problems of the patient are carved up very arbitrarily and apportioned to different disciplines not always to the benefit of the patient – the surgeon performs the operation, the nurse provides the daily care, the social worker looks into the possibilities of welfare benefits or tackles emotional problems and, on occasion, the chaplain is called in when a spiritual or a religious issue raises its head. This is what might be called multi-professional care. Each member of the professional care team does his or her best but may seldom if ever meet with the others to look at the patient rather than his or her problems.

What is aspired to in a hospice is better termed *inter*-professional care, where each person knows, uses and respects the skills of their colleagues, where each professional learns to support colleagues – in every sense a team, working together under its captain or leader for the overall good of the patient. There is a daily interprofessional meeting of the team so that each member is always up-to-date. The doctor will continue to be the one who diagnoses and suggests treatments but, equally important are the sensitive observations of the nurse, the insights of the social worker, the ability of the chaplain to identify and help with spiritual problems, all working in a seamless fashion, for the patient and his or her family and friends. Let me illustrate this with a typical scenario.

'She's very much more comfortable so it seems to me we can make arrangements to get her home to the care of her family and their GP. She doesn't look as frightened as she did', says the doctor.

'I agree she's better but she's still very frightened and asking us even more questions than when she first came in, so we nurses feel another day or two would help enormously.'

'We'd go along with that', say the physiotherapist and occupational therapist in chorus, whilst sitting quietly in the corner the chaplain says he wonders if even two days will be enough because she has begun to pour her heart out to him and he has pencilled in several hours to spend with her.

'I'm delighted about that' says the social worker 'because when I asked if I could help she said not but I had the impression there were many things troubling her but she just didn't want me to be the one to hear them.'

Such interprofessional working is undoubtedly effective but is not easy to achieve. Professionals are traditionally very territorial, jealously guarding their areas of responsibility and often are far from appreciative of others who seem to challenge their authority or their uniqueness. Doctors in particular find it difficult to appreciate that nurses are nowadays highly trained with well developed psychosocial skills. As the nurses are never slow to point out they are with the patients much more than any doctor is.

This then is the setting for the book, the place about which I was so often asked 'How would you describe a hospice and what it's like working there?' The book might equally well have been entitled 'Learning from the Dying', the title of a lecture I have often been asked to give to audiences around the world. That too would have been an appropriate title for, as one old gentleman once said to me, 'People talk about me as if I've died already, and I'm very much alive, you know.' Later in the book readers will come across the story of a teacher, his body hideously attacked by cancer but with a mind as intact and as sharp as ever. He it was who reminded me that as long as he was able to speak and teach in an effort to make the world a better place, then life was worthwhile. If that was his definition of the meaning of life, then he had a rich life and we were the richer for having been with him, to the end.

For the author one of the rewards of working with the dying has been the challenge of seeing how their teaching, their example might somehow help us to make the world a better place. Some of the 'discoveries', some of the insights, made in a hospice are so moving that one is compelled to ask how they could improve the quality of life for the living as well as for the dying. Could we make our society better if we practised something of what we learn in a hospice ? Would you and I be better people if we learnt from my patients and their families? Could it be the final irony that places established to care for the dying are eventually recognized as models of how we should conduct our lives and co-exist in harmony with each other and with our God?

I have subtitled the book '*Memories and Musings of a Hospice Doctor,*' for it is no more than that, the reminiscences and thoughts of someone who worked in hospice and palliative care for many years, who learned more than he ever taught, who received more than he ever gave. Those who are looking for a textbook will be disappointed, as will those who are searching for profound answers to life's greatest questions. This book, like the characters in it, poses many questions but offers few answers. Hopefully it will make us all think more about things which dying patients said were important.

Why the 'platform ticket'? Well, read on and decide for yourself.

Chapter II

Coffee Cups and Mugs

'Truth, when witty, is the wittiest of all things.' Keats

As everyone knows there are so many ways of showing our love. Sometimes it is in the giving of presents or pleasant surprises; at others in the warmth of physical contact or the sharing of secrets. We often demonstrate the love we have for our children in the way we protect them, taking their hand crossing the street or warning them against hidden dangers and innocent-looking strangers or even neighbours. Most of us seem to find it easier to show our love than to speak about it, or perhaps that is just a dour Scotsman speaking.

The threat of losing someone we love seems to bring out the most protective instincts in most people, sometimes to their great surprise. They go to amazing lengths to keep the fearful diagnosis from the sufferer, little realizing that the patient is probably also doing the same for them; mutual protection. This is something we see every single day in a hospice and never ceases to amaze, but how many people appreciate that even when people are dying they still find ways of showing their love. In fact, they probably work harder at it than they have ever done since their 'courting' days.

I remember being invited by a family doctor to visit a gentleman who had been ill with cancer for four years and was now entering the terminal phase of the illness, devotedly cared for by his wife of forty years. The doctor said that he would have sought my help much earlier had it not been for the embargo placed by the patient's wife. She had kept the diagnosis from her husband, and refused to allow any doctor, even the family doctor of so many years, to tell him the truth or to invite in anyone who might break that seal of silence and pretence. 'I suspect you'll have quite a difficult time with the lady,' he warned me, 'but there's no question she looks after him wonderfully. My problem is that I suspect he has questions he'd like to ask and can't. Even though I know them both so well I feel inhibited when I visit. She watches me like a hawk yet I'm pretty sure it would help him to talk things over. All the years I've known him he's wanted to know the truth and made certain he got it, even with the most trivial illnesses.'

When the lady in question answered her door bell there was apprehension written all over her face. In a warm, welcoming voice she ushered me into her sitting room and quietly shut the door which led into the hall and upstairs. Then, dramatically, her voice changed to a quiet, conspiratorial whisper. If ever there was a simple means to upset an ill person and make them wonder what is going on it is to open the front door with a flourish, greet the visiting doctor in one's normal voice then tiptoe in with him, whispering as you go.

'Just 'cos I've got cancer it don't make me daft or deaf, you know' I remember one old gentleman saying to his wife. If I had not been there I suspect he would have done an 'Alf Garnet' and called her a silly old moo but people are nearly always on their best behaviour with doctors around! However, back to the defensive lady I was telling you about.

'I want you to know that I'm grateful you've come and that I don't mean any disrespect, but', and here she whispered even more quietly, putting her face close to mine, 'he has not the faintest idea how ill he is and I don't want him ever to find out. I've managed to keep it from him for four years and I wouldn't like you or anyone else to tell him. I do hope you understand? When you've been married, as we have, for forty years you know your other half inside out – you can almost read their minds you know – and I know for a certainty that John does not know he's dying. Not the foggiest idea, I can assure you. Before I take you up to him I want you to promise me you'll not tell him.'

It was not easy but I tried to explain that hospice doctors, or palliative medicine specialists if you prefer that more correct title, are very sensitive people and have enormous respect for the love people have for each other. We don't go in 'where angels fear to tread' as the saying goes, announcing that people have cancer and are about to die, as if they had no feelings. On the other hand, neither do we deliberately tell lies to soften the blow or to make our lives easier, tempting as it might be. I warned her that if he asked questions I would answer them honestly and as sensitively as I could. I tried to explain that there must always be some bond of trust between a doctor and his patient. If he was to suspect that I lied with impunity that bond would be broken. She was clearly very apprehensive, far from convinced with what I had said, and near to tears. I strongly suspected that if she could she would ask me to leave.

'Just remember, doctor, that I've been married to him for forty years and I know him much, much better than you will ever do. If he ever learns that he has cancer it'll be the death of him! I shall hold you responsible.' I refrained from making the obvious but inappropriate response to that.

She went upstairs ahead of me, flung open the bedroom door and announced me with a flourish which would have done credit at Buckingham Palace.

'John darling, here's the specialist come to see you to make you better. Isn't that kind of him?' I would not have been surprised if he had replied 'Yes, mummy.'

John was sitting propped up in bed. It did not need a medical degree to recognize how ill he was. His face was gaunt, his skin yellowish and almost transparent, his eyes dark-rimmed and deep set in his thin face, but nevertheless bright and alert.

'I'm delighted to see you, doctor. Thank you for coming. I hope you'll have a coffee with me?' I gladly accepted. Most hearts open, and most barriers fall, over a cup of tea or coffee. 'Darling, would you like to bring us some coffee and also some of your special shortbread to show doctor what a wonderful baker you are?' They seemed very relaxed together but I was experienced enough to recognize that he was getting her out of the way.

He patted the side of his bed indicating that I should sit near to him rather than in a chair by the window. His wife went out to get the coffee and, asked to do so by John, shut the bedroom door behind her. No sooner did we hear it click shut and her feet pattering downstairs than he grabbed my hand.

'Delighted you've come! We've only a few minutes before she'll be back with us so let's get to business. I want you to give me your solemn word that you will not tell her what's the matter with me nor how ill I am. Believe me, she hasn't the faintest idea. We've been together now for forty years and I know everything there is to know about her. I even know what's she thinking and always have done. I can tell you that without a shadow of doubt it has never once crossed her mind that I might have cancer and that I'm going to die in the next few weeks, never once! I've spent the last four years keeping it from her. We've always been totally honest with each other about everything but when I found I had cancer it was easier than I thought to tell white lies. To me it was worth it so that she wouldn't worry or fret the way women do. Well, doctor, do I have your word before she comes upstairs with that coffee?'

I instinctively felt this was one of those unusual occasions when it would not be inappropriate to hold his hand or his arm lying on the bedclothes beside me. I did so as I spoke.

'Sir, what would you say if I told you we have just had an identical conversation downstairs? Would you believe me?' Our eyes never left each other.

'Are you trying to tell me she knows? That's impossible, quite impossible. How on earth could she find out? I presume, sir, you did not tell her, because if you did I shall be very angry. The last thing in the world I want is for her to know how ill I am. I shall go to any lengths to keep it from her. She must know where you're from, if you haven't already told her.' I shook my head.

'You have known for four years and kept it from her because you wanted to protect her because she means so much to you. What you did *not* know was that she too has known it from the beginning and done all in her power to keep it from *you*.'

Tears began to course down his cheeks. I sat silent, trying to understand something of what he was experiencing.

'If I'd known all this what a lot we could have talked about, what a lot we could have done to help each other instead of acting out this stupid charade for four years. How did I never guess that she knew?' This was a rhetorical question and both of us knew it. He took my other hand and squeezed it as he agonized with what had happened.

'Oh God, what a fool I've been! I've tried to protect and shield her all our life together and, of course, she's done the same for me. I really thought I knew her inside out; really believed that I knew what was going on in her mind. No-one will ever know how lonely I've felt and how many questions I've wanted to ask, but how could I do it when I was pretending that I was getting better? I suppose it's been the same for her, poor dear. I'll bet she's been lonely just at the time we most needed each other. Look out – here she comes with the coffee.'

'Here we are, gentlemen, coffees and shortbread . . .'

Her voice trailed off as her eyes spotted his tears rolling down his face on to the bed they had shared for so many years. At one and the same time she dropped the tray with a crash, spilling the coffee and breaking the cups and saucers, and spun round to confront me.

'How could you? After what you said to me downstairs, how could you? Oh, I was right. I told our doctor you must never be allowed in our house. Oh God, I hate you for what you've done!' She fumbled for a handkerchief and began to sob.

'Darling! Darling, listen to me please, Doctor hasn't said

anything – it's me who's done all the talking. You see, I've known about the cancer since they first diagnosed it. In fact, if I'm honest, I strongly suspected it before they started the tests. Don't ask me why, but it's true. I've known for years that I had it and that sooner or later it would be the death of me but I was determined that you would never find out. I'm not crying like this because I've got cancer or because I'm going to leave you – I'm crying because you've known and I've known and we could have been helping each other all this time. I've let you down. That's why I'm crying like a baby. I thought I was doing the right thing for you just as you must have thought the same about me . . . darling, come and let me kiss you.'

They both looked at me, still sitting there, a silent but privileged onlooker in one of life's great poignant dramas. He released my hand and, as men do, gave me a slap on the shoulder and the warmest of smiles. I stood up and moved towards the bedroom door.

'I think this is one of the times when a "kiss and a cuddle" is a doctor's best prescription for you both. When you want me to come back up and answer all your questions, give me a shout – I'll be downstairs.' With that I took her hand and led her to the bed where his hand was already outstretched to greet her, and quietly left them, closing the door behind me.

Only a few minutes later I heard laughter upstairs, followed by more and more laughter and finally a shout to come up and join them. They sounded like a couple of young lovers rather than a couple soon to be rent asunder by death. As I went into the bedroom I saw them both sitting close together on the bed, laughing as if they would never stop.

'You'll never guess what she's just said to me, doctor. She says this has been one of the worst days in our marriage and if it wasn't that I am so ill she would divorce me! Do you know why?'

'Oh, John, you are awful. The doctor might take you seriously! He doesn't know what an awful tease you are. Doctor, don't listen to him.'

'She says it's all because the carpet is ruined with that strong coffee and, because you are a specialist she had brought out the best china and now it's all broken! Isn't that just like a woman! Never mind, darling, I'll have my will changed straight away and leave you a little something so that you can buy yourself a new coffee set!'

She pretended to smack him but instead kissed him. 'You don't know everything, you old rascal. You don't know how much I love you.' Turning to me, tears welling up in her eyes, she said 'I'll get some more coffee now and you'll both just have to drink it out of our kitchen mugs. Men!'

'You'll never know what a relief it is to have it all out in the open. Until this happened to me I'd never known what loneliness was, you see. We'd shared everything – every thought, every fear, every problem, every joke, every tear . . . what on earth made us think we could keep *this* from each other, I shall never know. What a strain it was trying to tell lies every day when we'd never had a secret between us.'

Some people keep up the pretence, or the charade as we should probably call it, right to the end. They have worked so hard at keeping their secrets from each other that they convince themselves of their success and nothing, nothing at all, will make them change their minds. When they realize that, in some senses, they have failed, the pain and the distress they suffer must be intense, particularly when their intentions were so honourable.

I remember as if it was yesterday the day a gentleman was admitted to our hospice, accompanied by his wife. We knew from his medical records how ill he was and, like all the patients, he had already been visited by some of us at home. We all knew that there was no possibility of him ever returning home. What we had perhaps not been prepared for was the fierce protectiveness of his wife, a tall, well built, immensely imposing lady. A colleague who had seen me talking to her later bumped into me in the corridor and whispered as she passed me, 'Was that Boadicea I saw you with?'

'I've heard about you,' she said when I introduced myself. 'You have a reputation for being good with pain. You're just the man Roger needs because if anyone has suffered hell, he has! I've been very disappointed with you doctors up till now but perhaps you'll redress the balance. I've certainly heard good things about you.' I am far from immune to compliments and smiled in what I hoped would pass for genuine modesty and humility.

'Oh, I can certainly promise you we'll beat his pain. Leave him in our hands with absolute confidence.' I was unprepared for what followed.

'I've also heard that you have peculiar ideas about telling patients what's the matter with them. Poppycock, if you ask me! You'll not try anything of that nonsense with Roger, let me tell you. I have made it my responsibility to ensure that he was never told, never even given a hint, of what ails him, and to this day – as you will soon find out for yourself – he has not the faintest idea. He believes he has come in here for you to ease his pain and after you have done so he will return home and resume a normal life.'

We all remember times when even the drawing in of sufficient breath to reply seemed ages. This was one such, I was conscious that my mouth was open and air was going in ready for my first word but no sound came out before she had resumed her harangue, for that was what it had become.

'I am sure I need not remind you that I have been married to Roger for nearly fifty years. I know every thought, every fear, every question in his mind, None of them relates to his illness because he believes as surely as day follows night that he will recover. Have I made myself clear?' In a quite uncharacteristic way, I nodded assent. I was being honest, after all, because she had left me in no doubt whatsoever.

It proved easy to relieve his pain and, in fact, to make him comfortable in every way. He was a delightful person to care for, grateful for the smallest service, always asking how others were, not least the nurses, and eager never to be demanding or, as he put it, 'a nuisance'. As each day passed he lost more weight, became more frail and needed more sleep. Time was getting short.

One afternoon I passed his bed. He called me over and asked if I had a few minutes to answer some questions he had. One thing we soon learn looking after the dying is that an opportunity not grasped is an opportunity lost because it seldom returns. It is so easy to say, and to say in complete sincerity, that you are very busy but will come back in just a minute or two. When you do so the patient no longer wants to say something or ask that all-important question. I immediately went and sat on his bed.

'I've written down a few things I want to know,' he said, then with a smile added 'well actually that's not true. There are twenty-one questions and I don't just want to know, I *need* to know. All right if I ask you them all now?' I agreed and as one always does in this work, tried to give the impression – a totally false one incidentally – that I had all the time in the world and had he not called me over I should have been wondering how to fill in the afternoon.

'First of all, how long?' I must have frowned or shown some hint of embarrassment because he immediately went on. 'Come on Doc, you know perfectly well what I mean. How long before I pop off, die, fall off the perch or whatever you want to call it? Don't look at me as if I'm a damned fool – I've known since those first tests that my time was up, so let's have it. How long is there left – a week, a few days or is it going to be tonight?

'No need to spare my feelings, Doc. I've been in life's departure lounge long enough to know what happens. What time's my flight?'

Only young doctors believe they can tell a person how long they have left. As we get older and look back on a lifetime of mistakes in this field we are more guarded, choosing our words more carefully but trying never to hurt and never to lie. I told him I thought we were talking about a few weeks, but not days and not months. He seemed satisfied and glanced down at his list, written on the back of an old envelope.

'A lot of questions all in one, Doc. What will it be like, who'll be there, will I know what's happening, will it be painful and will I be muddled or demented, or whatever you call it, by then?'

I tried to answer them all for most of them were easy. Again he seemed relieved. The next questions were about calling his family and helping his wife ('she has no idea what's happening as I suppose you've noticed, no idea whatsoever. Thank God I've been able to keep it from her, poor dear. Never crossed her mind so far as I can see.') and then financial matters.

'Now Doc! A very personal question to you and I hope you'll not be offended. Are you a religious man, a church-goer as they say?' I nodded. 'Then would you mind spending the next few minutes helping me plan my funeral service, choosing the hymns and readings, and drafting the notice for the papers – all that sort of thing? It will be so much easier for Elsie if I get it all organized in advance. Pity I can't phone the crematorium and make a provisional booking, eh?' I smiled but found it difficult to laugh at what he clearly regarded as a wonderful joke.

Just when we were getting to the end of this very sensible but somewhat unusual exercise I heard the nurse coming, her voice deliberately raised to warn us of her approach. 'I think doctor is in with him but I know Roger is looking forward to your visit' each word getting louder and louder. She obviously knew or guessed what our conversation had been about.

No sooner had his wife come through the door than Roger greeted her with great excitement, smiling like a boy who'd found the cherry in the cake. 'Darling you'll never guess what I've just discovered. Doctor here,' and at this point he swung round in his bed and gripped my arm, 'may I call you Derek, is an authority on Spain and on cars. For the last half hour he's advised me on the best paradors where we should stay next year, mapped out the whole route for us and even suggested getting rid of the big car and replacing it with a smaller one more suitable for the narrow Spanish roads. Isn't that wonderful? What a holiday we've going to have and all thanks to him.'

I made my excuses and left hastily. What was perhaps most troubling me was not the contrast between what he knew and what his wife thought he knew but that at that time I had never once been to Spain and my knowledge of cars extended little further than knowing at which end was the engine. Perhaps I was still musing on a remarkable conversation and the even more remarkable drama of life but I was suddenly gripped by the arm and swung round. The lapels of my newly-laundered white coat were clutched by Boadicea who proceeded to shake me as if I was a disobedient puppy.

'Now perhaps you'll stop saying that all patients know how ill they are and want to talk about it. They don't! Perhaps you'll now give me credit for having protected him from the truth for the last few years and admit that I've done a good job of it. Would any dying man talk about going to Spain or be so excited about where he was going to stay? What sort of a fool do you take me for?' Thankfully she did not want an answer but loosed her grip on my coat and let me down!

With that, obviously feeling better having got it off her ample chest, she returned to his bedside to plan the Spanish holiday. For my part, I telephoned his GP and, in confidence, shared the conversation and the wife's reaction with him.

Ten days later he died, as peacefully as he had wanted and, like everyone, as he had deserved. Never once did he mention our conversation to me or any of the care team but none of us could fail to see how serene he was and to note that he needed fewer painkillers and nothing at all to help his sleep.

Carefully laid at the top of his papers, placed so that his wife would see them immediately, were the plans for the funeral service, his choice of hymns and his draft of the death notice for the paper.

The GP, who had known them both for many years, made a point of visiting her within a few hours of her getting home and described how devastated she was, not by his death which she had prepared herself for for so long, but by discovering how much he had known and managed to keep from her. He smiled as he recounted her reaction:

'Where on earth did he learn to act so convincingly?' she asked her doctor.

'I strongly suspect he had a wonderful tutor, a role-model as they say nowadays.' replied the doctor.

What a diplomat that doctor would have made but what a loss he would have been to family medicine.

Good stories but not typical, I hear you say. Oh, but they *are* typical in most respects. They illustrate the lengths people go to to protect those they love and also, dare I say it, to protect themselves. Some years ago a study was carried out in one of the major medical schools in Britain asking senior students why they found it so difficult to 'break bad news' as it is often called. The responses may look so predictable that we should not be surprised. The students did not want to hurt the patients in any way by telling them bad news. Associated with that, they were apprehensive about how they would handle the patients' reactions to bad news, whether it was their tears or their crying or screaming or whatever happened. All very understandable. They then went on to explain that they would rather not break bad news because of how it might upset them, the students, and because they might not be able to control *their* emotions in front of the patients. We never like to admit that some of the things we do are for self-protection as much as for the protection of those we love, do we?

Perhaps it is only when you have worked in a hospice that you truly appreciate, as these stories illustrate, that it is not death which people fear but the manner of the dying ,whether it be the pain or the fear or, as we are often told, the loneliness. Let me tell you a story which has become one of my favourites, a delightful story about a lovely old lady. It begins with me sitting beside her shortly after she had been admitted from her beautiful little apartment where we had cared for her for a few weeks. Now too frail to remain there alone but very comfortable and without any of the pain and anguish she had had when first we met, she was now settling in to her new and final home. I asked her how I, as her new doctor, could help her, knowing as I did that she was not likely to have much physical suffering. Her answer took me by surprise.

'Young man,' she said, making me realize that her eyesight must also be failing fast, 'I have mixed feelings about what lies ahead. If you can spare me a few minutes let me try to explain what I mean.

'A bit of me is excited, in fact very excited, just as you feel when you've seen a holiday place advertised in one of those glossy brochures but never been there and, more to the point, never even met anyone who has. It's also a curious feeling when you've only got a single and not a return ticket because you know for a certainty you're not coming back! The other thing I have to tell you is that I've had my bag packed for a very long time. Now that's a curious feeling too. It's a little bit like British Rail. You know the train will come but *when* is another matter altogether! You know it's no use asking anyone because no-one knows any better than you do! When you get to my age all these things add up to a very new experience, as I'm sure you understand. I'm one of those people who prefers the familiar to the new and untested, and I suspect I'm not unique in that.

'However, that is not the biggest trial I am facing, waiting for my train. Believe me, waiting on this platform is a very, very lonely experience even when the brochure said it was a nice place I'm going to, even when you have a ticket and even when you've been ready for the journey for a long time.

'You very kindly asked in what way you could help me. Well, let me explain so that you will understand. I am finding this the loneliest time in my life. I'm surrounded by nice people and everyone is so kind, but I'm still lonely and just a little frightened because' (and here she gave a timid laugh) 'I've never done this before, you must remember. Until that train comes in . . . well, I would love you to stand beside me. For that you'll need to purchase a platform ticket! Now do you understand? No, perhaps you don't because you are too young.' (She was not the sort of lady who would try to flatter her doctor so I was now sure her eyesight was gravely impaired.)

'When I was young they only allowed you to go on to a platform if you had a ticket for the train or if you had a platform ticket so that you could wait with your loved one or friend. They only cost a penny, in the old money of course, but what a joy it was to stand together a little longer at such little cost. I suspect we all like someone with us when we go off on a long journey, don't you think? I see you understand now.'

Each day when I went to see her she just shook her head and told me I was not needed. Days and days went by. Then one day, when she looked no different to me, she whispered 'Have you got your platform ticket?' I reassured her that I had and carried it with me wherever I went. She invited me to come and sit beside her, which I did.

'Oh what a curious feeling to be so lonely and at the same time so excited' she explained. 'We don't need to talk, you know, but I need to know that as that train comes in you'll stay beside me until I tell you. That's the point when I shall have to leave go of your hand and take that last step on my own. I know I'll manage if you are near me.'

It is difficult to describe atmosphere and ambience. Sitting with that lady was to experience a peace that is so rare in life. I think other doctors would agree with me that we are trained to talk but not how to remain silent. We are taught how to explain but not how to listen. We are taught how to be energetic but never how to restore peace and tranquillity by our inactivity. We are taught nothing of inner peace, nor of loneliness, and nothing whatsoever of the power of love and undemanding companionship. Those minutes which followed were some of life's richest for me.

What privileges we enjoy in our profession. My musings were abruptly cut short.

'At last!' She turned to me and smiled. Her thin hand squeezed mine as she whispered 'Sometimes we need doctors and sometimes we need friends. It's best of all when our doctors are also our friends. Thank you, dear, for being my friend. You cannot come any further but don't worry. I can manage now.'

Her grip loosened. I turned and looked at her. She had never moved. On her thin, lined face there was a hint of a smile. She was dead.

I sat for a few minutes pondering on what had just happened. I thought back to the years I had spent training as a physician, striving to understand and practise modern scientific medicine, taught and inspired by brilliant men whose shoes I would never be able to fill. Understandably they had never mentioned platform tickets but neither had they alluded to the many other skills I now found I needed, ministering to the dying. I had been taught how to teach and how to speak, not how to listen and how to hear what was really being said in myriad ways.

I had been told about anxiety and the distress it can cause but given no insights into the crushing power of terror. Never had I appreciated that loneliness, rather than aloneness, was like a cancer which seemed to suffocate. No one had told me that love can at one time be healing, and at another be dangerous and damaging unless it is totally self-denying.

I looked around me at a world with which I thought I was very familiar and where I felt at home, the inside of a hospice, looking in most respects little different from any small, homely hospital. Familiar and safe to me, but what does it feel like to a person who knows it is their life's departure lounge? What makes a place safe for one and frightening to another? I registered that as a question to be answered, as something highlighted by the hospice but probably relevant wherever we care for the ill and frail.

I realized I would have to give much more thought not only to platform tickets but to the whole of that journey so many of our patients were taking. What was it our patients really wanted of us, their doctors and nurses? Were my scientific and diagnostic skills to count for nothing? Do patients need something we have not got to give them?

One day I too would be waiting for my train, presumably like my patients, fully aware of all that was happening no matter how well my friends had protected me, but would I be ready for it and, I was anxious to know, would there be people there with their platform tickets? Perhaps that was up to me, I thought. As someone brought up in the Christian church my mind went back to the story of Jesus in the Garden of Olives the night before His execution. What He had most wanted and hoped for, but did not get, was for His disciples to stay awake and keep Him company on what must have been the loneliest night of His life.

I suspect much of this book will, in one way or another, be about platform tickets.

Chapter III

Detective Work

'To die will be an awfully big adventure.' J M Barrie

There are some people who believe all this talk of quality of life should be listed as a health hazard. They see it as patronizing and highly insensitive to be speaking of people who are going to die very soon and in the same breath to be philosophizing on the quality of their life. To them the two are mutually exclusive. I should not be surprised if they did not ask that the health hazard was brought to everyone's notice at the entrance to the hospice in the same way that the dangers of smoking are printed for all to see on the cigarette packet.

As one cynic asked me 'Does anyone go into Death Row and ask the inmates about their quality of life? Does a condemned man ever sit discussing what you doctors refer to as quality of life issues?' (Recent reports from the USA suggest that in fact they do but that is another matter.) 'It is an oxymoron to speak of dying and quality of life in the same breath,' say the critics!

'How can you hospice doctors be so cruel as to talk to them about dying?' they ask. Better to keep patients in the dark, only telling them anything if they ask, and even then as little as possible, as used to be the teaching. There used to be an adage that the less the patient knew the happier they would be, the thinking being that we are all eternal optimists. It never crosses our minds that there is anything wrong until it is too late to worry. Why upset someone unnecessarily?

As the patients in this book are teaching us, nothing could be further from the truth. Quality of life rests on many things, just one of which is informed insight into the details of their illness and its seriousness. It is not how much they know that matters, but, rather that they are always told the truth and given as much information as they feel they need at any one time. People appear to suspect the worst before they are 'told', but more of that later.

The days are long past when doctors received no training whatsoever in communications skills. Some of their paternalism has gone, hopefully for ever. They have been affected by consumer reports which listed poor communications as more distressing than almost anything else in the health care system, apart from possibly the waiting lists. The problem is that they are more often taught how to explain than how to listen; taught 'how to break bad news' rather than how to respond to perfectly reasonable questions, embarrassing as they be. Doctors often feel that they have done their duty and fulfilled their obligations when they have 'told' the patient. Their duties are only starting. It is not the fearful diagnosis which scares most people but the prospects of what life will be like in the run up to death, or, to put it rather crudely, it is dying they fear rather than death itself.

Furthermore it comes as a surprise to many of us, doctors and relatives, to discover how patients learn of their diagnosis. A little bit like the relatives we spoke of in the previous chapter, doctors assume that everyone remains in ignorance until told by the doctor, while relatives, as we have seen, convince themselves that they can and must keep everything unpleasant from their loved ones until they die. According to our patients, who after all should know best, we are all deceiving ourselves.

How then do people critically ill with something as serious as cancer or heart failure find out not only what ails them but how serious it is?

I was once asked to see a gentleman in a large teaching hospital. When I introduced myself without saying my speciality he shook my hand and said 'Oh, so you're a doctor for people with bad cancer, are you?' I wondered how he had found out about his illness and what it meant.

'Do you remember who told you?' I enquired.

'Nobody "told" me, if you mean saying something I did not know already! What happened was that I had my suspicions and my suspicions were confirmed. Not the same thing as being told, doctor!'

I asked him, and subsequently scores and scores of others in the same position, what had aroused the suspicions. The answers were fascinating, and for me as a doctor, eye-opening and embarrassing. Let me try to share what they told me.

Everyone said they had suspected there was something seriously wrong right at the beginning of the illness, even before their family doctor had ordered the many investigations and before he or she had referred them to the hospital specialist. In other words the first seeds of suspicion were there and starting to grow even before the results of x-rays and scans and blood tests were known, long before any doctor endeavoured to explain or called in colleagues to help.

Why were they suspicious, I enquired? Age was one reason. The older the person the oftener they had seen people in the same situation as themselves, often with the same symptoms and having the same tests. As one old lady said, rather bluntly but poignantly, 'When you get to my age you've seen an awful lot of your friends off at the crematorium so you've a good idea what's the matter when you get the same symptoms!'

How easily we overlook the wisdom of the old. One wizened old man once said to me 'When I was a young man and had indigestion like this I'd have blamed the spaghetti and Chianti I had gorged on the night before, but I'm not a young man now. I've seen too many friends carried off with stomach cancer to be fobbed off with the pasta and plonk explanation.'

Family histories played a part in fostering their suspicions. As most people know there are exceedingly few hereditary cancers, their genetic blueprints passed on from one generation to the next. What we do encounter are what have come to be called 'cancer families' who seem to be particularly prone to certain conditions. Most, but by no means all, of the women get breast cancer and many of the men get prostate cancer. It stands to reason that when a lady from such a family feels a lump in her breast she suspects it is cancer before she thinks of innocent cysts.

Their suspicions were subsequently heightened even further by something I, for one, had never known, namely the time it took to make the diagnosis and the range of investigations done before that. 'You don't normally spend two or three weeks in hospital, having your whole body x-rayed and gallons of blood taken for tests if you've got 'flu, do you doctor?'

'I'm not a fool, doctor – I know they don't have to operate on you to check if it's an ulcer! I knew then it was something serious and one look at the surgeon's face afterwards just confirmed my suspicions. His face had "bad news" written all over it, but instead of telling me whatever bad news he had he went on about arrangements for me going home.'

Some people suspected a serious diagnosis by the time it took the doctors to diagnose it beyond all doubt, others by the less-than-enthusiastic treatment they were then offered. 'It took them several weeks to find why I was getting all that pain in the tummy and back and then when they say they've found the cause what do they do? Nothing! They send me home and tell me not to worry because my doctor will be able to give me pain killers. When I ask is there not to be an operation they say it won't help and when I ask if there is not a specialist somewhere who knows all about this trouble they say they are the experts and there isn't any more that they can do. It stands to reason it must be serious if it took them so long to find it and when they can't do nothing . . . well, I ask you! It's clear you've got the Big C. Fancy telling me to get pain killers from the GP! It was because his painkillers weren't working that I went in to the hospital, after all.'

That seems to be the crux of the issue. Patient after patient said that all their suspicions were confirmed, not by what doctors *said*, but by how they acted, how they behaved. I believe this is now more usually referred to as 'body language'. Let some of their anecdotes speak for themselves.

'You usually go in to your GP and in a jiffy he has found the problem and written out a prescription. He has the air of someone confident and competent in all he does. He knows he'll have you well in a few days so off you go. This time when I went in he sat and listened and I could see the smile falling off his face. He'd never examined me so thoroughly before but instead of saying what was the matter he started to book x-rays and do blood tests. I went back for the results and instead of launching into his explanation – and I must say he's a good explainer – he looked terribly serious and said seeing a specialist might be a good idea. I knew the score when he said my appointment would be in two day's time!'

A lady explained. 'When you first go into hospital the senior doctor, the consultant or specialist or whatever you call him, comes round to talk to you' she said 'and so he sits beside you in a very reassuring way and explains that they will have to do many tests but, he promises, they will keep you informed and soon they'll know what it is and how to treat you. His tone is very warm and reassuring and he sits so close to you that no-one else would be able to hear what he said. You begin to wonder if you've been worrying unnecessarily. A few days later, after all the usual blood tests, x-rays, scans and goodness knows what else, the big man comes back with quite a few other people and they look at your results but say nothing to you. Someone holds up an x-ray and they all suck in air. This time he doesn't come anywhere near you but stands at the foot of the bed surrounded by what looks like the twelve disciples. They all talk amongst themselves then he looks at you over his half moon glasses.

'"Well, you haven't got anything that some special rays won't help and possibly a course of injections afterwards if you need them. I suggest we get you home now and I'll write to your doctor and he'll keep me informed how you get on. All the best!"

'With that the big man and his retinue moved on in stately procession, only the most junior doctor staying behind to whisper that he'll come back later and explain everything. By the time he had done so another woman in the ward, having listened in to the ward round as everyone does, had come over and explained what those "rays" were. She knew all about them because her husband had them for *his* cancer before he died! ("God rest his soul").'

As another man put it 'If a doctor gives it to you straight, explaining everything, you're OK because they never, never do that if it's cancer! If it's the Big C doctors waffle! Know why? It's because they're upset, they're embarrassed that they can't cure you, that's why.' I asked him to explain a bit more because this sounded new to me and very interesting indeed.

'Are you actually telling me you patients can tell whether or not your illness is serious by the way we explain it to you?' I enquired.

'Doctor, I remember one time I was in a hospital and the head doctor came and stood at the end of a man's bed. All his minions or whatever you call them stood around the bed staring at the poor patient. The head man then proceeded to tell him he had hardening of his arteries, that his heart had been damaged and that he was lucky to be alive. In a booming voice so that all of us could hear he said it was because he smoked and drank more than was good for him, and that he ate the wrong food, making him as fat as he was. He warned him that if he didn't mend his ways he'd soon be dead.

'They all went on to the next bed where he told a man all about his ulcer – he used that word ulcer – and said it had been caused by his smoking and drinking and poor meals. I felt quite sorry for him because he was a policeman and everyone knows they have to grab a sandwich and wolf it down when they get a chance. Both these men had been told exactly what was wrong with them, hadn't they? In each case the doctor had sounded really convincing.

'Then they came to the bed next to mine. The man had had hundreds of tests done and looked just awful. The head doctor went on about shadows in his chest, special penetrating rays he might get and the possibility that a surgeon might be able to help – waffle, waffle, waffle – but never once did he say what was wrong with the poor man. You ask anybody who has been in a big hospital and they'll all tell you the same. If the doctor gives you its name, you're safe. If he doesn't, you've had it!'

Of course, occasionally, a doctor gives a name to the condition but it is not the correct name. He elects to use an innocuous name so as not to alarm the patient but that ploy seldom works. I once pulled up my chair next to a lady's bed in one of our famous teaching hospitals so as to be able to chat to her in relative peace and privacy. I told her my name and said her ward doctors had asked me to come and see her in case I could help her in any way. Did she know what was wrong with her, I enquired.

'Oh yes, doctor. I've got' (and here she almost shouted) 'bronchitis. That's what the doctors have told me. I've got bronchitis.' At this she looked around to see if any of the doctors working nearby had heard her then she turned back to me and pulled me closer so that she could whisper. 'Actually I've got cancer but I don't want any of them to find out that I know because they're all so young and kind – I don't want to upset any of them when they've worked so hard to keep it from me.'

Amongst the many other 'pointers' described by patients who successfully deduced the nature of their illness, was the obvious embarrassment of young, inexperienced nurses when the patient tried to ask them about his illness; relatives returning from the other side of the world when they had never planned to for years and could scarcely afford the fare. ('I knew the score, doctor, when my plumber son walked in because we'd all had to club together to buy his ticket only six months before. Don't expect me to believe he's making millions, like he said.')

It came as no surprise that the biggest 'give away' was the whispering on the doorstep. Is there anyone who has not done that, either at home or in the hospital corridor, often in full view of the patient?

'I knew there was something very wrong, doctor, when the GP and my wife spent half an hour whispering on the front doorstep. It was either me being so bad they couldn't tell me or there was something going on between them, know what I mean!' said one man. 'I knew it wasn't *that* so it had to be about me. If I'd had something ordinary like 'flu they wouldn't have done that now, would they?'

I recall once being briefed by a ward sister just at the entrance to the ward before I went in to advise on one of her patients. We were actually standing there because her office was being used by someone else and the doctor's room was also unavailable. Nevertheless it was insensitive of us to stand there in full view of all her patients. Eventually I went to the patient she had pointed out to me. 'Hello doctor. Was she telling you I'm dying, that it took so long?'

Naturally I was able to take advantage of that and turned the questions back on him. 'No, actually she never mentioned you were dying. She was telling me all about the appalling pain you've been suffering and saying how much she hoped I'd be able to help you but since *you* mentioned dying – are you?'

To be fair, as we must, the situation is vastly better than it used to be and is improving steadily, but far too slowly. Doctors are trying harder than they have ever done to recognize the subtle pointers to what the person knows and wants to know but it can be incredibly difficult to do.

I was once involved in the care of a very young lady, in her twenties if I remember rightly, who was a gifted musician. She played both cello and flute. Her cancer was now out of control and had spread to many of her bones, some of which had broken as a result. To make matters worse she also had seedlings in her lungs. The result was that she seldom had enough puff to play her flute and when she sat legs straddled to play her cello she suffered pain in both thighs. She was one of those people, and there are many of them let it be said, who want every bit of information possible but find it too painful to ask directly. They prefer to ask questions like conundrums. We all knew that her gifts and talents were so amazing that she could master a new instrument within six months. The way she found out how long she still had to live was to ask me one of her 'trick' questions.

'Sometimes I haven't enough breath for my flute and it's quite tiring holding my cello so I wondered if I should take up piano?' This question betrayed so much. She knew her lungs would not improve and might get worse, just as she knew the cancer in her bones would make it not just difficult but eventually impossible to play her cello. Her question was not whether she would live but what would the next six months be like, if she was spared so long. How subtle but also how typical of the questions people have but cannot ask directly. The challenge to the doctor is, as it were, to have a built-in short wave receiver to pick up the messages which otherwise would be missed, or as one colleague once said in my presence, a good doctor has unusually long antennae to hear the things which were never said.

The more articulate and educated the patient, the more he expects to be told. Today most people are 'told' something and deduce the rest. The problem, as this little book illustrates, is that it is not usually the diagnosis which frightens people but what it means for the quality of their life. It was Hippocrates, known as the father of medicine, who said that 'old men fear dying, young men fear death'. More than two thousand years later that is still true. We cannot get away from talking about fear which is itself about information, both of which affect quality of life.

Years and years of working in a hospice convinces you that quality of life is at the heart not only of hospice and palliative care but of life itself. If we professionals spent as much time and thought in restoring and maintaining that quality as we do in finding ways to prolong life, how much better it would be for us all.

Here we are again speaking of quality of life. No wonder some people complain or they might ask why we don't spend more time looking at quality of care. Perhaps it is time to ask what people mean when they speak of quality of life. Does it have any meaning or has it just become one of those buzz words or phrases of which we seem to have so many in our modern society, part of our twentieth century jargon?

Let's ask the patients themselves. It is after all their lives and their feelings we are interested in.

We have already mentioned the cynic who scoffed at speaking to the condemned about what they regard as quality of life as they wait for execution. I believe the comment was truly cynical for two reasons. The first is that having a terminal illness for which you are not to blame and for which you are receiving the most skilled and compassionate treatment bears no resemblance to being in so-called Death Row. The analogy is not only inappropriate. It is offensive. The other reason is that, though I have never tested my thesis, I suspect even condemned prisoners can differentiate between a good and a bad day, between a day they will be happy to look back on and one they would rather forget as quickly as possible. I say this because we are all human beings with a remarkable similarity between our emotions and our responses to other humans. Whoever you are, wherever you are, you can recognize kindness just as you can see tell the difference between good intentions and evil intentions, unless you are psychopathic. Hospice care reminds us all that, under the skin, aside from that awful life-threatening illness itself, we all have a very great deal in common. It is this which makes it possible for people to describe what *they* understand by quality of life.

37

There seem to be no less than four ways people quantify it and try to describe it.

Go to one man and ask him what constitutes a 'good day' for him as opposed to a 'bad day' he would rather forget. Understandably he will talk of pain and suffering. Any day when he has had to endure those is a bad day, We need not dwell on that because the relief of pain and suffering lies at the heart of hospice and palliative care. That is exactly why hospices were established, why we have the medical and nursing specialties. It is almost inconceivable than anyone will speak of life having any quality when they are still in pain, particularly when that pain is unnecessary as most pain is.

That aside, you put it to him, what makes a good day? His answer may be 'making people laugh and forget their troubles.' When you ask him about his past life and then speak to his family you find that he has always been a *bon viveur*, the 'life and soul' of the party, someone who always had a joke or saw the funny side of things. He has never been a professional comedian or entertainer, but everyone agrees he has been a great companion, good to be with, good to count as a friend.

Given that knowledge you know he will gauge a day by whether he has brought a smile to someone's face, whether he has made someone laugh, whether he has turned someone else's tears to a smile. When you ask 'what sort of a day have you had' rather than 'tell me about the quality of your life?' he will tell you a new story, or sometimes an old one which he hopes you have never heard before (as we all do) or perhaps recount how he made someone happy that day. How well I remember such a man we looked after. At the end of the late evening round I dropped in to his room in the usual way to see him. 'Doctor, sit down for a minute while I tell you a joke. You look exhausted and need to get home to your bed but this one will keep you laughing all the way home.

'Did you hear of the man who was dizzy, faint, confused, weak

– everything felt to be wrong with him? He went to his doctor who examined him very very carefully but could find nothing wrong. The doctor said to him "I cannot find what is wrong with you. It may be the drink." So the patient said "Not to worry doctor. I'll come back tomorrow when you're sober."'

When he had told his story and we'd both had a good laugh he pointed to the door.

'Don't ask me if I've had a good day, because of course it was good to make the doctor laugh like that. Good-night.'

Someone whose faith means a great deal to them will also have their way of evaluating a 'good day', though of course there's no reason why they aren't joke tellers as well. They will tell us that a good day is one when they feel alert and comfortable enough to read their Bible or to pray, or perhaps, given the opportunity, to tell of their faith to someone else. These are good people, in the best sense of the word, and it must not be thought we are describing religious fanatics who make the lives of others a misery with their triumphalist religiosity.

So many beautiful things happen late at night in a hospice. This story I am going to recount is no exception. It was long after ten, almost all the main lights were out and the few people still awake could be seen under the gentle subdued overbed lights, some reading, a few just sitting and thinking, a few watching the nurses going about their duties. The soft light over a bed gives a very peaceful feeling though you can scarcely see the person's face. In fact, because it is partly behind them it gives an impression of a halo. Those ladies who are propped up in bed often have a silk or crocheted woollen shawl round their shoulders and in all the ladies' rooms there is usually a delightful smell of perfume or bath soaps. Televisions are off (one is tempted to say thankfully), but a few people are obviously enjoying a CD or the radio on their 'Walkman'.

As our doctors all did, I was walking round the rooms to see that they were all comfortable and 'safe', speaking to one here, waving back to another over there, and wondering, as I always did, at how peaceful it could be even in the shadow of death. At these times there is a great sense of mystery and wonder, a profound sense of honour, being permitted to minister to people at the end of their lives.

She was a frail little lady, silver-haired, and like so many people with cancer, looking a good deal older than she really was. She waved in greeting then changed the wave to one of beckoning me to sit on the edge of her bed.

'Don't say a word, doctor. Get that Bible over there on my locker and look up a little passage I want you to read.' I did as I was asked and obediently found the passage and began to read as she lay back with her eyes closed.

Come unto me all ye who labour and are heavy laden and I will give you rest. Take my yoke upon you and learn of me; for I am meek and lowly in heart and ye shall find rest unto your souls.
For my yoke is easy and my burden is light.

I finished, closed the Bible quietly in case I wakened her because I was sure she'd fallen asleep but as I did so she opened her eyes and smiled at me.

'Isn't that a reassuring passage? Even when you are tired, as you are tonight doctor, God knows and understands and can help you. I imagine that there are some days, and this may have been one, when you wonder if you can keep going and here is God saying he can help you even when you can't help yourself.' Before I could say anything, and what was there to say apart from thank you, she reached out and held my hand.

'It has been a hard day for you today hasn't it? We guessed that from the nurses, bless them. What wonderful people they are. I stayed awake in case you dropped by so that I could bring you a little bit of comfort with a passage that has often helped me. You've made my day.'

Of course, it has to be admitted that every coin has an obverse side. There are just as many people who find it difficult to live according to their faith and witness to it when they are critically ill. They have a miserable quality of life and feel profoundly guilty. All their lives they have regarded it as the foundation of their living, the lynchpin of all their hopes and dreams. Now, suddenly, it seems inadequate, irrelevant and their despair knows no bounds.

We have described how some define their quality of life in terms of spreading happiness whilst others feel everything has been worthwhile if they can help others through their faith. It was one of Britain's most famous and influential doctors who suggested we look at the frustrations experienced by people with advanced cancer, because that might well be a way of measuring their quality of life.

No one would deny that every illness, even a mild one, entails frustration. Even being unable to swallow because of a sore throat is frustrating so how much worse must it be when you have advanced cancer. A man would love to be walking on the beach with his dog but, because of the cancer and what it is doing to him, he even needs assistance getting out of bed. Some, to everyone's surprise, accept their physical limitations, but what a burden their mental ones are. A distinguished legal expert once told me he could accept not being able to walk around his flat. He could even accept that he needed assistance to go to the toilet. What he could not accept was that his memory was poor, his concentration span only minutes, and he was consequently finding it well nigh impossible to complete the encyclopaedia he had been working on for years and years. I could not help wondering what he had been like in his better days because I found his intellectual acuity daunting. Yes, no one can deny that serious illness, whether or not it is life-threatening, leads to frustration. This frustration can make life a misery. The worse the frustration, the worse the misery or, to use our new-found term, the poorer the quality of life.

The answer to that frustration is two-fold. The first thing we can do, and how paradoxical this must sound, is to lower their expectations to make them more realistic. The second is to work on their ability to do things, in a sense to rehabilitate them, so that they can do a little more than they thought possible. I tried to explain all this to a patient once, fully expecting him to be offended because it could sound so patronizing. To my surprise he grasped the concept at once.

'What you seem to be saying is that instead of lying here moping and miserable because I want to be climbing the hills I should set my sights on things that I *can* do. You're saying I should be thinking about getting out of bed without help, and then walking around the room without help, and then walking down that corridor before I talk any more about hiking. Right?'

'You've got it.' I replied.

'In that case *you* have a job to do as well as me,' he replied 'because you and the team will have to get me stronger and show me how to walk. If I have to lower my sights a bit – and that's a big thing you've asked me to do – I expect you to help me to do more than you think I can manage. It seems to me we have to work together to set realistic goals, haven't we?'

What a revelation. How often do we ever think of terminally ill people setting achievable goals with their doctors and nurses and physiotherapists? A good day, for them, becomes one when they achieved their goal and managed to set a modestly more challenging one for the next day. Achievement became a reality, albeit a small one, and frustration gets less and less by the day. This is something everyone can understand.

Let me illustrate the fourth way we can look at quality of life with some more true stories.

One afternoon the nurses told me that a patient seemed very 'down'. They had no idea why and she would not discuss it with them. She just admitted that she felt despondent, very different from her normal self. I went in to see her but had little hope she would say anything to me if she would not tell the nurses. She was actually crying when I sat down beside her and asked if I could help her.

'Well, I'm crying because of you, if you must know, doctor. I realized today that I'm no use to anyone any more. No one needs me; I'm not interesting to anyone. It's the first time in my life I've felt utterly useless. I never thought this day would ever come. I might as well be dead if I'm no use to anyone.'

I was appalled. What had I done? The answer was simple – I had not used her as an example when teaching the medical students who had visited the hospice that morning but I had taken students to several of the other ladies. She assumed she was no use, of no interest to anyone, valueless! Readers will not need to be reminded that we give a great deal of thought to whom we invite to help us with medical students, particularly when the patients are frail and often emotionally fragile. I had not approached her for permission because I thought she needed some peace and rest, not because she wasn't 'interesting' any more. The lesson is that we all need to feel wanted, valued, even interesting. I wonder if many of us have stopped being fascinated by the people we meet or the people we work alongside; by what they say or how they say it; by their mannerisms or their interests, their beliefs or their wisdom.

It was rare for our occupational therapist ever to be stumped but it did happen once. A man had been referred by his GP as much for the sake of his long-suffering wife as for his own sake. To say he was cantankerous was an understatement. If you said white, he said black. If you said yes, he would always say no. If someone suggested this, he would always say the opposite. He seemed to feel that he had been sent to us as a challenge. He was right. He was the only man I have ever met who sincerely believed that everyone else was out of step except him, and to make matters worse, we were given to believe that this had been his life's pattern, rather than the result of his illness. His wife was the first person I ever encountered who said she looked forward to her husband dying because only then would her life be worth living. The occupational therapist was at her wit's end. What activity could she give him which would be worthwhile and not merely time-filling. She found it.

By next week he was making a beautiful range of wax candles in every shape and size. Not only that, he was teaching others how to do so (and doing so with consummate skill). Like many crafts it was not as easy as it looked and fellow patients, and even some of the volunteers, sat around the table watching him with unqualified admiration. He became a different man.

I went and stood beside him at his worktable one day but he was too busy to stop what he was doing and just gave me a brief interview!

'You see, doctor, this is all very remarkable for me. It's the first time in my life I've felt I could do anything useful. The first time I've been wanted by anyone. It makes you mad to realize you have to get to the end of life before anyone spots how clever you are. I've never been needed before, do you realize that, doctor? In my whole life no one has ever said "We need you".'

Well, not quite true I feel sure but who was I to say. He died a very happy man and his wife, just as we expected, missed him terribly.

What point is there in all this defining of quality of life or, more correctly, in these different ways of looking at the quality of life? I suggest quite a lot. Each person seems to have their own way of doing so. The man who loves to bring a smile to peoples' faces has always been like that and always will be. The visiting doctor, or even the relative, can focus on that knowing that if he can make someone else happy he will be a happy man. We learn how useful it is to remember jokes or stories we can pass on to such patients to be recounted later. When we visit him, instead of the traditional

'Hello. How are you today?' we can ask if he has any good stories or any new jokes. There is no danger in that because we know for a fact that that is what makes him happy. He will soon tell us if he is 'down'.

We can respect the religious person and ensure that in every day there is a time or a place set aside for quiet and prayer. Surely it is very easy to ensure that everyone feels wanted or needed in some way instead of being either a fascinating disease or, as they are so easily made to feel, a burden on our society and its over-stretched budget.

My illustrations may sound pathetic to some but I can only say it was effective and it was much appreciated. We tried to find ways of helping everyone to feel they had a role to play; one would be asked to buzz on the patient-call system when someone's relative came in or when a frail neighbour needed the help of a nurse. As many as possible were asked to help when the medical students visited; others read for a fellow patient or wrote a letter for them.

When people sense they are approaching the end of life they are desperate to know they have achieved something, that all they have gone through in life has not been in vain and that, to the moment of their death, they are somehow needed and valued.

As usual, let a patient have the final word.

One day, before the medical students came, a patient asked if there was any way she could help, adding as I suspect she had always done because she had such a low opinion of herself 'though I don't expect there is anything interesting about me.' She was poorly educated, had had an appalling life of deprivation and poverty, been badly treated by two husbands and now had cancer, rapidly spreading through her body. Most of us might have been bitter or full of self-pity after such a life but not her. She exuded kindness, making it a wonderful experience to be with her. I went in to see how she was with a lady medical student sitting beside her and the look on that student's face said it all. She was obviously unaware of my standing near her so spellbound was she listening to the patient and that remarkable tale she had to tell. As she left I heard her thank the patient in a way which was clearly totally sincere. 'I am so grateful to you for letting me talk to you. You've taught me more than you'll ever know. May I come back and see you if I get the chance?'

'Fancy that, doctor,' said the patient a little later when I went in to thank her. 'No one has ever said that to me before. Fancy anyone wanting to come back to see *me* of all people. I don't remember when I felt so happy.'

Chapter IV

Quality Control

'A time to break down and a time to build up.'

A feature of hospice and palliative care almost unique to Britain, is the Day Unit, whether called that or the Day Hospice. It caters for people under care at home but fit enough to be brought into the unit for the greater part of the day.

What goes on in a Day Hospice is surprisingly difficult to describe to anyone who has not visited one. It is a hive of activity but, surprisingly, can also be described as a haven of peace. Some patients are busy doing craft work while others are doing what human beings everywhere like doing, sitting and enjoying watching the workers. To say it is diversional therapy would miss the point completely. The therapists are helping them with activities which will develop latent skills and make maximum use of their limited energy. Possibly, for a very short time, a few people stop thinking about their illness and what lies ahead for them but just as many are very conscious of it.

It has been said that 'a Day Hospice re-affirms living rather than focusing on dying'. Trite as that may sound it is certainly true. People coming for the first time are understandably apprehensive and tense but in no time are so relaxed that when they go home that night their relatives are asking what drugs they have been given! Said one old lady who had obviously had a terrible life with her husband 'I wish I'd had whatever it is you give him thirty years ago! He was a great wee man before we got married then the drink went to his head. Thirty years of misery, that's what I've had to endure, and just when his end comes in sight you lot give him some magic pill. It's no fair, sure it's not! Why did our doctor no ken about it?'

What had happened was that the Occupational Therapist had been talking to him and he'd admitted that though he loved his wife of so many years, he'd never been able to tell her. Now that he was so ill he wished there was some way of telling her that he loved her and appreciated how she had put up with him when others might have thrown him out. The therapist knew just what to do. Even though the most delicate operation he had performed in the previous twenty years had been lifting a glass to his mouth, as he often used to tell us, she taught him how to make an red enamel brooch in the shape of a heart. Quite dextrously he had put in the fine powder, then placed it in a miniature kiln, and when the job was done, taken it out and fastened on a little chain which the therapist just happened to have in her box of tricks. A little gift box was found and lined with cotton wool. It was ready for him to hand to his wife when he went home. Magic! We had a suspicion it was the first present he had ever given her, but she could not have been happier if it had been a Fabergé egg.

With typical medical confidence I had told his GP that he was so ill that I expected he would only be able to attend the Day Hospice for a few weeks before having to be admitted for terminal care. Day Hospices do amazing things to many patients. One is giving them a will to live. Another, for reasons we do not understand, is changing the pace of the cancer, apparently slowing it down in some people. More than two years later one of our nurses asked me would I care to revise the prognosis I had given! Why do nurses ask questions like that?

I spoke of latent talents. I suspect we all have them but they usually remain latent, never getting the chance or the encouragement to develop. It must seem a contradiction in terms to say a hospice is an ideal place to do so but such is the case. Even more surprising is that most people have no idea what lies hidden within them and never imagine that in their last few months or even weeks of life, something will develop and flourish.

We had a policy of always asking patients both what their hobbies and interests were and what they had always wanted to do but never got round to it. The first part of the question was easy and predictable. People would list their interests as television, dancing, DIY, reading, travel and so forth. Surprisingly many people say they have no hobbies. The second always evoked an embarrassed smile. 'Promise me you won't laugh if I tell you something I've never told anyone before?' and then they would tell us how they wanted to learn to type, or to use a word processor, or to paint with oils or even how to cook a special dish.

We are all familiar with that old joke about the surgeon telling his patient that when the plaster came off his arm he would be able to play the piano. The patient was delighted because, as he explained, he had not been able to play the piano before the plaster was put on. It sometimes seemed like that with some of our terminally ill patients. People said they wanted to cook a particular dish then admitted that they had never cooked anything, or said they wanted to paint something but had never drawn or painted in their lives. Maureen was just such a person.

She told us her greatest ambition was to paint with oils. What she did not tell us was that she had never drawn anything in her life, and had never even painted with water colours or poster paints. A volunteer was recruited to help her but she did not realize he was a professional artist. He was amazed at her latent skill. Twice a week she came into the Day Hospice and soon a remarkable painting of a vase of flowers began to appear on her canvas, without him ever putting a single brush stroke there for her. Before it was finished she had to be admitted to the wards but the easel was put on the table by her bed. Her partner and several of the nurses gathered round the bed to see the final brush stroke. Too weak to keep her arm up she asked him to support her. The painting was complete and truly remarkable. 'That was what I have always wanted to do. Now I can go.' She died a few days later, her painting beside her, a beautiful reminder that the right encouragement and the right atmosphere can do so much.

People used to tell us of the most surprising ambitions. There was the man who had never had the benefits and pleasure of a secondary school education who told us he had always wanted to learn how to use a personal computer. Needless to say he never thought his wish would be granted just weeks before he died but when he mentioned it we immediately had a PC brought in, a volunteer recruited to teach him and in no time he was thoroughly enjoying himself. He knew full well how little time was left to him and was disappointed that he might not be alive to see the Queen when she visited the hospice. He therefore put a message of welcome on his computer screen for her to see as soon as she walked into the Day Hospice. It was a deeply moving scene when we showed it to her and explained that the gentleman who had put it on had just learned how to use it but was too frail to be with her.

A member of staff once remarked to me many years ago how tired she was of people asking her if it was not depressing working in the hospice. Eventually she gave them all the same answer. 'The only depressing thing about the place is the number of people who ask that question who should know better!' In a Day Hospice there is always something happening, someone laughing or singing. As visitors always remark, it is a positive place.

There is one time when there is absolute silence but an all-pervading smell of wonderful cooking, a smell which seems to permeate through the whole hospice. One of television's Master Chefs of the Year is demonstrating his amazing skills. It is Gerry, for long a friend of the hospice, an architect, a wonderful painter and more recently a charismatic chef who has come back to tantalize us all. A little group of patients sits round a large table next to the oven in the Day Hospice. From a handful of ingredients he seems to be able to make the most wonderful dishes, tasty, colourful and smelling so delicious. People who have scarcely eaten for weeks enjoy every mouthful. Those who still have some strength and energy left go home that afternoon determined to make one of his dishes for the delight of their loved ones.

Doctors and nurses all seem to find reasons for being in that part of the hospice and drop in, as they hasten to explain, 'just to assist with quality control tasting.' Somehow suffering, pain, tears and fears seem to evaporate when there are people like Gerry sharing their love and their skills in the hospice. What's more, as in every hospice, they do it without any thought of payment or advertising, their only reward being the faces of their audience when they taste the food or see some other finished product.

A patient once told me that before he developed his cancer, and was still enjoying good health, he had once heard me lecturing on hospice care and referring to 'quality of life'. 'I completely agree with all you said,' he remarked, 'but it is much more than that. Hospice is not just about quality of life. It's also about "meaning of life". It is much, much more than freedom from pain, answers to your questions and all that. It is about sharing, giving without wanting anything back, about the power of love, about accepting your fellow human beings.'

This giving without expecting anything in return, this unconditional generosity comes as a surprise to many people when they see it in hospice care. Perhaps they experience it as a patient. Perhaps they see it when they visit loved ones. Others who remark on it are the medical students, arguably the last people you would expect to comment on it when there are so many other new things for them to learn about.

Is it a reflection on the times in which we live that we are surprised when we see unconditional love? Have we grown so accustomed to people always putting a price on what they do, or expecting some expression of thanks, that we cannot believe it when someone gives of their time or their skill and expects nothing in return? I suspect so. How sad.

One of the first patients ever admitted to our Day Hospice was what the world would describe as a very successful man. He had recently retired as one of the most senior officers in the Air Force. His origins were humble, but his ambitions had been limitless. I doubt if even he knew the extent of his wealth but whether his happiness had ever equalled his worldly success was doubtful. He could name hundreds or even thousands of acquaintances, but less than a handful of real friends. Twice divorced, with grown-up children who scarcely ever saw him, he was cynical about human kindness, seeing it as weakness. His philosophy was simple, as he never ceased to explain to any near enough to be trapped by him.

'If any man works hard he deserves to be paid, that's what I always say! What does it say in the good book? "Every man is worthy of his hire." I've no time for people that work and say they're doing it just because they want to, or because they want to help those less fortunate than themselves. If someone can't help himself, he's not worth helping, it seems to me! Hard work never hurt anyone and we shouldn't need help from charity. That's my philosophy.'

Not only was his philosophy a little hard to swallow. So was his obsessional personality. Wherever he went he carried his A4 size notebook in which he recorded everything and the precise time it occurred. When you greeted him and said it was good to see him he'd look in the book and report that he had arrived at ten hundred hours and been given his cup of coffee at precisely ten o nine hours. We could all keep a straight face at this but found it a little more difficult when, as one has to when examining him, we had to enquire about his bowel function. 'Thought you'd ask, Doc! 0 nine hundred hours, one motion approximately ten centimetres in length.'

Not the kind of talk to win friends but dying brings out the best in people, crude as that may sound. We watched from the touchline, as you might say, to see how fellow patients would react to him. In their better days most of them would probably have given him the kind of answer his cynicism called for, matching him word against word until each had said his piece, but not now. For days no one rose to his bait. The volunteers kept on caring as if nothing had been said. Cushions were plumped up to make them more comfortable, help was given when feeding was difficult and always there was a helping hand ready when someone else needed to move around the room or be taken to the toilet. Always quietly said, most often just whispered, were the many 'thank yous' as genuine appreciation shone from the faces of those who would far rather have been the helpers than the helped. His rudeness and arrogance fell on deaf ears.

Attending the Day Hospice at that time was an old chap whom we had first seen in one of the worst slums in the city. After much persuasion he had agreed to come one day a week, as much to give his long-suffering old wife a break as to help him. Tearfully she had told us, in the most graphic detail, what a delightful man he had been before they were married but the past few years had been a living hell with him. He had taken to drink, been in and out of work, had often beaten her and brought home little to feed their children who, understandably, had left home at the first opportunity. Would it be unkind to describe him as one of the most miserable, ill-mannered, ungrateful men most of us had ever encountered?

On his first day there he sat and scowled, agreeing to remain until the car came for him at 3 o'clock only if he could have a can of beer to drink in peace. The next visit he began to come out of his shell and soon was not only chatting but pleasant. In no time he was helping others less mobile or capable than himself, giving a hand here or a word of cheer there, seemingly always seeing the need before anyone else. He was a changed man and a positive delight to know, uncouth and uncultured as he was.

One day we saw him sitting down beside our resident cynic. 'Do you know what's the matter with you?' he asked.

'Of course I do, man. Do I look a fool that doesn't know what's the matter?'

'It's not your cancer I'm talking about. I'm talking about something much, much worse than cancer and you've got it bad! You're blind! You can't see love when it is staring you in the face! You can't recognize that you need it, I need it, we all need it but what's more, everybody here has it, except you!' He almost spat out those words in the face of the man who must seldom have been spoken to like this in his life, and certainly not by a man so lowly he might never have addressed him.

'I came here just as bitter and disappointed as you and I never had the chances you've had in your life. I despised "do gooders" and I thought this place would be full of them. Then my eyes were opened. They never ask if we are good or bad, if we have money like you or nothing like me. They don't even expect thanks. They are not doing it because they have to but because they want to. When I came here I thought I knew the meaning of love' and with that he turned round to see that they were not being watched and then winked at his listener. 'Now I've found the real meaning of love. It's what makes people do this and it's what's making me speak to a man like you.'

The wealthy cynic sat motionless, only his eyes following every movement of the speaker. He was transfixed. The little old man got up from the low chair he was crouching in and looked down at his companion, this time speaking a little louder as if wanting us all to hear him.

'Tell me if there is anything I can get you or do for you. On the other hand, if you're feeling a bit better today and able to do more, perhaps you'd like to help me assist some of the other folks, will you? I could do with your help! You could make a start by drying those mugs and after that go round and see who wants more tea.'

The retired officer can never have been spoken to like this in his life but without a word of complaint he got up and started to look after the other patients. The silence of the room was broken by our little old man. 'Oh, and don't you dare write down all I said and what time it was when I said it!' To the officer's credit he saw the joke and began to laugh with everyone else.

'I wouldn't dare with you watching me, you old battle axe.'

Two men changed beyond recognition, not by their cancers and certainly not by the medical treatment they were receiving. Men changed by kindness, shared experiences and shared need.

Until they both died several weeks later, these men were almost inseparable.

Once, chatting to an actor who was visiting the hospice, I remarked how difficult it was to describe the Day Hospice. I told him how some people seem to change and how it often brings out the best in people, somewhat to the surprise of their loved ones. He listened, said nothing but smiled. I asked him what he was smiling at.

'It sounds to me as though your Day Hospice is like one of our rehearsal rooms. We use them, as the name implies, to practise being someone else without being laughed at. It's where we feel safe to try out things, like new voices, different walks, and strange mannerisms. It's vital that we have somewhere people won't laugh at you.'

How true that is. In the Day Hospice everyone is accepted however much of a fool they are making of themselves! We could do with a few more places like that in this world.

Chapter V

Ripples of Laughter

*'A time to weep and a time to laugh; a time to mourn
and a time to dance.'*

It would be grossly dishonest to say that there are not many, many
sad times in any hospice. There are. There is bound to be sadness
when someone's death brings to an end a happy marriage or
deprives little children of a parent. There is bound to be sadness,
often tinged with anger and bewilderment, when a young person
dies, just as we find ourselves asking why some old person, long
ready and eager to go, lives on hating every minute of a life of
dependency and little dignity. Where is God in that, we are often
asked?

Never a day passes without someone angrily telling us of the
colleague in some other hospital who seemed unable to understand
their need and unable to make himself or herself understood. Every
week a long-lost relative from the opposite side of the world appears
on the scene and proceeds to take matters into his own hands,
demanding to see the consultant, writing letters of complaint about
someone else's mishandling of a situation, bur seldom
acknowledging that he or she has scarcely been in touch with their
family for the past twenty years. How often anger is a smoke screen
for guilt!

Someone once described a hospice as a place of laughter and
tears, like the warp and weft of a fabric, interwoven and somehow
creating strength in spite of apparently being opposites. It is
profoundly true. Perhaps that could be a description of life itself, a

balance of laughter and tears, of happiness and sorrow, of hope and despair. We seem almost unable to survive with only one component and if we do, we are not very interesting people.

Cynics, and there are many when you mention the word hospice, would say that any humour to be found there must surely be black humour, gallows humour, any jokes being at the expense of the dying, Nothing could be farther from the truth. Earthy, occasionally vulgar perhaps, but never unkind. The elderly gentleman who, without thinking, said he had just had a bath with Sister was certainly not setting out to offend but made everyone, including Sister, laugh. Perhaps we all found it especially funny because the nursing sister he was speaking of was also a nun, and one of the most beautiful ladies you could ever wish to meet, though she would be the last to admit it.

It was not often that we had a hereditary peer as a patient but he became part of a joke when a nurse said to us 'I've just given the lord an enema' to which the chaplain added 'God moves in mysterious ways.' Not drawing room humour perhaps but enjoyed as much by his lordship and the patients as by the carers and, surely quite innocent and innocuous.

There was one occasion when a joke was enjoyed by all the visitors, all the staff and all the patients except one, the gentleman who made the comment. A patient's daughter was a brilliant clarsach player (for those unfamiliar with it, a diminutive Scots harp). Mother asked if she might be allowed to bring it in and play it for her. We were delighted to agree. So beautiful was her playing that in no time people were coming out of their rooms to listen to her. A hush came over the unit as conversations stopped and people came to listen. Doors were propped open so that bed-bound patients could also enjoy it. Soon the whole place seemed transfused with this heavenly music when suddenly a confused old man called out from his room 'Tell that b***** angel to shut up. I've not come to heaven to listen to that all the time!'

As any music therapist would tell us, music has amazing powers.

It can bring peace to one and excitement to another, memories of happiness as well as of trouble. Within minutes we can be transported to holiday scenes or be back in our childhood. I only have to hear Elgar's Nimrod Variations to be sitting in the Assembly Hall at school waiting for the Founder's Day Orator to be led in by the headmaster, or hear Bach's St. Matthew Passion to be back in student days listening to the lady later to become my wife singing it in the Usher Hall, Edinburgh, leaving me and everyone else there spellbound at such music and such singing.

In the world famous palliative care service in Montreal, Canada the music therapist used to make special tapes to suit each patient's needs, perhaps helping one to relax and get off to sleep, another to combat his pain. We were never so sophisticated in our hospice but we deserve credit for trying with one patient. Sadly he was muddled and confused, as many can be in their final weeks, and somehow nothing that we did seemed to bring him peace. A relative came and asked had we tried Hawaiian music! 'You know what I mean – the sort of music them Hula Huka girls wiggle to.'

Keeping a straight face we said no, that was the one thing we had not thought of. Was it possible it might help? Without any doubt, we were told. All his life whenever he had been cross or unhappy he had put on an old record of the Hawaiian electric guitars and in no time he had been quiet as a lamb. That record was duly brought in and, lo and behold, it worked. The agitated, restless old man was pacing around his room like a caged bear one minute and the next was lying back in his chair as peaceful as anyone could hope to be.

Just across the corridor from him was another man, never known to smile and certainly not the type to tell jokes, or so we thought. Hearing the Hawaiian music wafting on the tropical breeze from the other room he started to moan and groan, obviously distressed. Staff rushed to help him only to be told that he was always upset by that music. The only thing that might help him now was to see some of those beautiful dancing girls swaying in front of him!

Minutes later one of the nurses entered, her improvised grass skirt made of raffia from the Day Hospice, her shoes and tights off, swaying alluringly to the music of the South Seas. We witnessed an instant cure. That night I asked an anxious looking patient if I could help in any way, only to be told that unless I could dance like that nurse and look like her, I had nothing to offer.

An encounter with a patient at home with her feathered friend still makes us smile. The nurse and I visited her after her GP had phoned for some help and support. She ushered us into a large sitting room, very characteristic of late Victorian buildings in our city, and introduced us to a large grey parrot sitting on his perch in a huge cage almost filling the bay window. She pleaded with him to tell us his name, say hello, but to no avail. All we got was a look of disdain so we turned to the more important business of getting the lady to tell us of her problems and how we might help her.

The time came when I needed to examine her but rather than going through to her bedroom she suggested we looked at her on the chaise longue in the sitting room where we were. When I needed to examine her 'back passage' as we euphemistically term it, as one always does, I explained this to her. No sooner had I finished than the previously silent bird squawked in the loudest voice imaginable 'Oh no you won't! Oh no you won't!' Shortly afterwards we left her, still wondering how and where the bird learnt to say that.

Interwoven into that fabric, however, are also the tears. The tears of self-examination and self-discovery, the tears of regret and disappointment. How often do we hear people start their sentence with 'If only . . .' How right Bernard Shaw was when he had St. Joan say 'If ifs and ands were pots and pans there'd be no need of tinkers'. Hospices are full of them but has it helped those of us who work there to be different? I wonder. Not a day ever passed there without some patient telling us how he regretted not doing

59

something, or not saying something, instead of putting it off till another day.

By an interesting coincidence we once had two ladies with exactly the same name in a four-bedded room. They were both in their eighties, both very devout church ladies, both more than ready 'to go' as they put it, and both deaf (though they would vehemently deny that as they shouted to each other). Every night they could be heard praying aloud (both assumed that God was deaf though they were not) and respectfully telling him of their readiness to meet him sooner rather than later. Each morning they awoke and, as surreptitiously as possible, looked to see whether the other 'had gone'. We all loved them, the Misses Marples of this world, and envied them their graciousness and olde world charm. Neither of them ever had a cup of tea – it was always a dish of tea. Sandwiches were always cucumber. It was impossible to imagine either of them even understanding a swear word, far less using one, and as for losing their temper, inconceivable!

One morning, however, all hell broke loose. One had died during the night and the other, wakening up and seeing that she had not been the selected one, began to tell God exactly what she thought of Him. He was asked what He thought He was doing, if He was deaf, if He ever listened to what she said to Him, if He had any reason for taking the other one and not her. Then, all of a sudden, there was a pause, a very long pause. Silence. 'You didn't by any chance get our names mixed up did you? It's easily done. I've made mistakes like that myself, I have to admit. I'd understand if you'd made a mistake because we all make them! I have to say, however, that it's probably all been because you don't always hear what we say to you.'

We could scarcely control our laughter as we stood nearby in the corridor and listened. We had no option but to listen when God was being spoken to in such a booming voice. She must have softened in her criticism of Him because she finally added 'It says in the Bible we are made like you which suggests to me that you also make mistakes and get people mixed up as I do. If that is the case I hope it won't happen again and I'll speak to you again tonight.'

I think it was the first time I had felt sorry for God.

Perhaps for me the best piece of that story was its sequel, what another patient said in the adjoining room. She had heard every word, as had all the patients, for obvious reasons. This lady was very frail and knew, as we all did, that she might die at any time.

'I suspect that if I meet God today He'll still be laughing at that one. I know I shall be.'

Somehow funny events like that seem natural in a hospice, just as much to be expected as the tears and the pain of self-discovery.

Laughter and tears, smiles and grimaces there certainly are, as families are re-united or torn asunder, friendships are forged or someone dies, never once visited by family, with not a friend in sight. Hospice means safety for one and fear for another; new-found happiness or sense of purpose for some and family feuding for another in the room next door. How could it be otherwise? That is simply a description of everyday life.

Would anyone expect it to be all happiness, all smiles, all serenity? Surprisingly the answer is yes, they would. That someone should not want a loved one to die is totally understandable but that they should expect antidepressants to reduce their grief comes as a surprise to many of us, yet that is what many asked for. Perhaps we should not have been so surprised because people are always asking their doctors for something to help them sleep after a loved one's death or drowning their sorrows in alcohol, neither of which are effective or helpful in any way. Many people seem no longer to accept that life has to have its troughs as well as its peaks, its horrors as well as its laughter. Is that, as some have suggested, because our society now has higher expectations, expectations that often seem to be unattainable. Are they expectations of ourselves or just of others, of society as a whole or of the immediate community in which we live?

Is it that today there is a low tolerance level for the unpleasant? Or, serious as that is, is the problem more profound than that? Have we lost the ability to cope with the unpleasant and, more importantly, have we forgotten how to learn from the bad days of life? Perhaps we are a society less interested in our yesterdays than in our todays. Perhaps we are a society which spends more time dreaming of its Utopian tomorrows, than how it can make today better than yesterday. That it is intolerant of all suffering and scornful of any who would claim we can mature as a result of suffering, seems to be beyond doubt.

I once enjoyed a chat with a musician who was visiting a friend in the hospice. Like me he was fascinated by history and what it can teach us. We got round to discussing how so much that is good and beautiful has blossomed out of sadness and misery in one form or another. He reminded me about Beethoven, tormented by his deafness and the isolation and bitterness it created yet his creations will surely be listed amongst Man's greatest for hundreds and hundreds of years to come. That took us on to talk about Tschaikowski and all he suffered as a result of his homosexuality, Schubert and his short life, Chopin composing such inestimable beauty whilst dying of tuberculosis and Schumann rejected and reviled by his teacher and father-in-law. Our memories flitted from Nelson Mandela to Helen Keller, from Ghandi to Martin Luther King. None of them was a stranger to sadness and disappointment yet each left this world a profoundly richer place, or so it seemed to both of us as we sat there philosophizing. These men and women and thousands of others had known the awesome gloom of life's darkest valleys and, perhaps because of that, revelled in the warm sun on life's peaks.

As so easily happens when two old men sit over their coffees our conversation moved to our contemporaries, those 'ordinary' people from whom we had learned so much, men and women who, in worldly terms were disadvantaged or even insignificant, but who had affected our lives. I told him of a teacher who had lost both his legs in the war but somehow we boys never seemed to notice his limp because he was so active, such an exciting teacher and role model. I recalled another master who could even make Shakespeare come alive but who was, as they would say today, a 'nervous wreck' having watched from his prison camp when the second atomic bomb fell. On a very personal level I knew how my life had been inspired by a grandmother paraplegic all the years I knew her, yet never once had I heard a word of complaint or seen a tear of self-pity. If I had an ounce of compassion or modesty in me it must have come from a father who since long before I was born to the day he died had carried the scars of war – partial blindness and lungs damaged by poison gas.

Pain and suffering, we both agreed, were not experiences to be sought but neither were they unqualified disasters from which could spring no good. The pity was that any good which might flow from disaster was usually only seen as such with the wisdom of hindsight. Even sadness and pain can be creative, almost cleansing, reluctant as our modern society seems to face that fact. The challenge, it seemed to us both, was how to enable good to come out of sadness and loss; how to recognize good, strange as that may sound.

My new-found friend asked me, as people often did, whether having a faith helped at the end of life. Obviously a man of faith himself, he reminded me that several religions, and in particular Christianity and Judaism, have suffering and pain at their heart but out of that deep pain and loss there comes happiness and meaning. Whether you believe in it or not there can be no doubt that the hideous crucifixion at the heart of Christianity followed by the promise of reconciliation with God as its result, are very compelling associations.

He understood when I qualified my answer by saying that it was bordering on the pretentious to say we knew what was happening in someone else's heart at the end of life. All I could do was give some impressions and pass on some things that people had said to us. I had to tell him that for some it is a time for confirmation of religious beliefs, for others a time of indescribable, unimaginable disappointment or disillusionment. For almost everyone, patient or relative, professional or visiting friend, it is a time for self-discovery. Discovery is always exciting, occasionally upsetting but, without exception, fascinating and revealing to the onlookers, the nurses and doctors and therapists who work there.

In recent years people have made much of the difference between *religion* and *spirituality* and, as you would expect, this has considerable relevance in a hospice. Now is not the time to embark on any deep study of these words, even if the author was qualified and able to do so, but a difference between them there most certainly is.

Religion describes a belief system, with its doctrines or dogmas, and their observance, including prayers, confession, scripture studies, liturgy and so forth. To many people it is immensely important, indeed a central part of their lives, and nothing of what follows should be taken as denying or diminishing that fact. The author has had the inestimable privilege of working closely alongside Christians, Muslims, Hindus, Jews, Buddhists and Taoists as well as animists. He has developed a deep respect for many of these faiths and for those who live their lives according to them. He has also to admit to some scepticism and many misgivings when looking at world history and the part denominational differences and religious dogmatism have played in it.

Spirituality is often defined as a search for existential meaning. Presumably since Man first began to communicate through primitive language and began asking questions he has wondered why he suffers so much, why he must die, why his god does not always answer his prayers and why he seems to deal evenly with the good and the bad. He must always have asked what is the meaning of life and whether or not anything follows this earthly life, whether we are reincarnated and whether morality, 'good living,' helps anything except our conscience.

'Spirituality is asking why, why, why and only getting more questions and never any answers,' a sage is said to have observed, to which the cynic replied, 'but each religion claims to have all the answers.'

I think it is correct to say that you cannot be religious without being concerned about spirituality. You can, however, be concerned about existential questions without being interested or involved in religion. That is very strongly borne out in a hospice where the perennial questions about Man, life and its meaning are always being asked but where most people, representative of our population, have little formal religious belief or church affiliation, cynical as that may sound. Studies have recently found that less than ten percent of our British population have an active church affiliation.

It might be asked how anyone can measure someone's church affiliation. The answer, given to me by one of our chaplains, was to ask them three questions. The first was their denomination, the second the name of their church if they said they were a member of one, and finally the name of their current minister or priest. It is very likely, he explained, that if they can supply all correctly they are keen, active members to whom their church means a good deal. On the other hand, he went on, if when they are asked what denomination they belong to and reply Christian and cannot recall being in a church they may be fine people but not formally religious. Of course this begs the question whether or not one has to attend church or have any church connection to have a faith. The answer is a resounding no just as, presumably, no-one would ever claim that only religious believers possess the virtues of love, kindness and self-denial. I omitted to ask the chaplain how you categorize the person with memory loss who cannot remember any of the answers and soon forgets the questions!

Scepticism, even cynicism, about formal religion is a common experience in those who have witnessed much suffering. Talk to those who have fought in wars or seen hundreds of thousands dying through famine and you often find profound respect for Man and his suffering but little time for formal religion. In fact the commonest words used when hospital or hospice patients chat about *formal* religion are 'hypocrisy', 'denominational differences' and 'pettiness'. What a contrast to their descriptions of personal faith when they speak of its importance in their lives and how, as they grow older or frailer, it takes on richer meaning – often to their great surprise.

To return to what we were saying about spirituality in a hospice! Here is the most obvious place, the ideal place, to ponder on Man's existence and ask those questions. Here there is time to think, every reason to ponder, and even people to ask. Here there is the greatest incentive they have ever known, their own nearness to eternity and the end of all they have ever known. 'Forgive me, doctor,' said an old gentleman telling me how he felt, 'you have to understand that I've never died before!' What a daunting time. What a responsibility for those who minister to them.

Whether or not they have pain or sickness, whether or not they can sleep or eat, move around or are totally dependent, they are all suffering in myriad ways. They have learned how to cope with life's challenges and how to survive but now all that is to change. Everything familiar will disappear as they go into the unknown, alone, often feeling ill-prepared, and more than a little apprehensive. As that same elderly gentleman went on to say, 'I thought I'd experienced everything and knew how to cope and now I find myself facing something I've never done before. At my age that's quite a challenge. Familiarity is such a comforting thing, isn't it?'

Why all this suffering, why this agony of seeing loved ones desolate? Does any of it make sense? Does suffering ever have meaning? Victor Frankl, one of the most eloquent survivors of the Holocaust, looking at the meaning of life and the place of suffering has said that suffering is bearable only if it has meaning. How then do we find any meaning in suffering? This imperative is infinitely more important that asking the question 'why' just so that we might lay blame on self or others. Looking around for someone to blame is what most people instinctively do today in our critical, reproachful, litigious society, but it is such a waste of time.

'Why did I get this lung cancer when I have been a Church member all my life?' asks the man who fails to add that he has also been a cigarette smoker for most of his life. Surely a rhetorical question. 'Why was I never told alcohol was bad for my liver? Why do doctors never tell you *anything*?' 'If they can send men to the Moon why can't they cure me?' 'Why do stupid old fools go on living for years and years and yet people like my mother have to die so young?' Are answers needed to these questions or should we be asking, are there any answers? Do we actually need any answers?

More profound and disturbing, and dare we say more important, are such questions as 'Why must a man who has led a healthy upright life die in his thirties leaving a young wife and their small children?' 'Why do some people, and some families, seem to have nothing but "bad luck" throughout life, from poverty and abuse, to desertion, divorce, hunger, to an early and horrible death?'

Sometimes the horror of someone's life almost overwhelmed us in the hospice, making us ask how so much could happen to one person and, more importantly, how one person could survive it as they had done. There was the young mother of twenty-five with her four little ones, her permanently unemployed, seldom sober husband, his criminal record as long as your arm, and her rapidly advancing cancer. We had to find ways of looking after her at home because there were no relatives willing or able to look after the children; no-one to go to the shops for her and not a single person prepared to help in the house when she was too ill to do anything for them. A more loving mum to her children, and a more stoically accepting wife, one could never expect to meet. One day I sat chatting to her, appalled and overwhelmed by the story of her life. 'What a desperate life you've had, so hard, so unfair. You must feel it's all been so cruel.'

'Oh, I never thought of it that way. I've never known anything else. My father was always beating my mother, and both of them were often drunk and then beat us kids, and so it wasn't any great surprise when they said I had cancer. Since I was so high,' indicating the height of a three year old. 'I've known that living and dying were really the same thing. If you want to know, I'm keen to see if it's any better in the next place.' She laughed at the thought then added 'It could hardly be any worse.'

A masterpiece of understatement was when an old lady was brought in to see her two remaining children, a son and a daughter, both dying under our care. 'Difficult to understand why I'm outliving them both!' For me that matched the thought expressed by one middle-aged man who said he was sorry to be dying because 'I've learned so much about myself and about life whilst I've been in here that I might have been of some use to others if I'd lived. The funny thing is that I've learnt a lot about me but I don't think I'll ever understand God!'

A common accusation often heard these days is that hospitals and even hospices are doctor dominated. To use that awful modern jargon, they all use 'the medical model'. Basically what that means, and it is meant to be pejorative, is that there is assumed to be a cause and effect in everything. Identify the problem, find the cause, treat it, and that should be the end of the trouble. Some might call that scientific (though it is not) and most would regard it as over-simplification of complex problems but, be that as it may, that is the way many doctors have worked until recently. Perhaps the Americanism 'Quick Fix' best describes it. 'You tell us the problem, we'll fix it. There's sure to be someone, somewhere who knows how to fix your problem because every problem has a solution if you know how to find it.'

It is, to my mind, a pity that one only hears talk of 'the medical model' in a critical, condemning connotation because our search for causes of illness and suffering has been of inestimable good to mankind in a vast spectrum of health issues. Where would most of us be if doctors had not identified our symptoms, sought the underlying cause and treated us appropriately, so bringing us back to health and vigour. It is the medical model which contributed to the eradication of smallpox, the reduction in so many infectious diseases, and so on.

Where it might hinder rather than help, as has now been so widely recognized by many doctors, is that much of man's suffering is not amenable to the medical model. It is a gross over-simplification to assume that a prescription will cure suffering associated with social deprivation and all its attendant ills, will reverse the devastation caused by war and privation, human greed and Man's inhumanity to Man, and be of any help with profound religious and spiritual anguish.

We return to our hospice and to the challenges we face confronted by spiritual questions put to us. Here, if ever an example was needed, is a time when the medical model is inappropriate. There are no slick answers, no cures, no reassuring phrases. The worst thing we can do when confronted by someone asking why, why, why is to respond with trite platitudes.

I believe our only response is to acknowledge the legitimacy of the question and to admit that we not only do not have an answer, but that we too are asking that same question as Man must have done since time began. For some reason that sharing of our humanity, that acknowledgement of our incompleteness and yearning, is more helpful than words can describe. This is one of those times in hospice care when being a doctor or a nurse or a social worker is secondary to being a fellow traveller on the road of life, sentimental or romantic as that might sound. That is what the old lady meant when she said she needed a friend more than she needed a doctor at that particular time. I suspect we often forget that human need. That is surely what Jesus of Nazareth meant when he asked his friends to 'Watch with me', in other words to keep him company when times were hard and loneliness was positively painful.

A young but wonderfully mature medical student was sitting in my office saying goodbye after spending six weeks in the hospice, a time that he described as one of the most exciting of his short life. He was recounting some memorable experiences. 'You know, none of the patients here seem to be interested in how clever a doctor you are or what higher qualifications you have. I suppose they assume you know what you're doing. What they want is someone who seems ordinary, if you know what I mean, someone who listens without giving answers, someone who enjoys being with them even when, like me, he feels useless.' I suppose what he had learnt was that platform tickets come in useful, but he was so young he might never have seen a platform ticket.

Is there a word to describe what we have been talking about? Is 'safe' still the best word or should it be 'peaceful' or 'reassuring' or what? Again it was a patient who said 'safe to ask questions' was a good description, or 'safe to be unsure'. In a world where so much store is put on certainty and predictability that make a hospice quite attractive, doesn't it. I wonder how many big multi-national companies would offer a job to an applicant who was honest enough to answer to a question 'I don't know'?

Of course, that may not apply to religion. People seem to win their 'Brownie points' in the church for their certainty and conviction, not for their doubts and questions. Those whose faith is so strong, so well-tested that it supports them through every experience of living and dying, deserve our unbounded admiration. There are many of them and, I believe, they are worth describing and talking about.

Almost without exception those whose faith proves more than adequate, and is an inspiring example to many of us, are those who never speak of it. They live it, they live by it, and scarcely if ever allude to it. They have no need to. In their presence one is aware of something more than a strong personality or a lovely disposition. There is an aura of unsophisticated goodness which words cannot describe. You feel honoured to be with them, honoured to serve them, honoured to be able to learn something from them, but their teaching will be by example rather than via a text. With few exceptions their deaths are as peaceful as their lives, unobtrusive, undramatic, uncomplaining, and serene. Is this what is meant by 'the Peace of God which passeth all understanding'? I suspect it is.

Then there are the others! Those whose faith has to be proclaimed from the rooftops, those whose 'Damascus Road' experiences have to be retold to everyone they meet, whether they have time to listen or not; those who would have you believe that they are facing death with all the courage and the confidence of a Christian looking towards the cage from which the lions will soon appear. Their language is the language of Canaan but, dare I say it, their faith has often not progressed beyond the earliest Sunday School days when they sang 'Twinkle, twinkle little star', ideal for those far-off days but woefully inadequate for a man or woman who now more than ever before in life, needs a 'thought through' faith which has been put to the test. I once heard it said that what we need as we face life's great hurdles is 'campaign faith, not choruses faith.'

I have seldom seen such tears of anguish as when a retired professor of divinity confessed to me that he had been preaching and teaching the Gospel for more years than he cared to count but never once had he ever thought of his own dying. 'Now that the time is so near, doctor, I am terrified. God forgive me, but I keep asking if His promises are as true as I have always said they are. I am so frightened, so petrified now that my time has come.'

'No, don't bring me the chaplain, doctor. He's a fine, fine man and I have nothing against him, but when I am so unsure of everything, so full of questions and doubts, the last thing I want is someone who is so utterly certain.' So said a lady a few days before she died.

For many, their unquestioning, unchallenged fundamentalism has been like an insurance policy, a guarantee that come what may they would get preferential treatment. 'The safety net of faith' I have heard it called.

Work in any hospice soon demonstrates that life is not like that. Young believers also die young and leave families, as unprepared for what lies ahead as any of us would be. Believers also have pain and suffering, experience fear and panic, like everyone else. They are no different from anyone else when they ask why, why, why? What is, to my mind, so sad is when rather than challenging or enquiring of their God as others might be tempted to do, they direct their anger against the world, blaming one, accusing another, kicking out at all and sundry. Is it any wonder that a hospice team often expresses apprehension when they hear such a person is being admitted under their care. 'Oh for a silent believer!' an agnostic colleague once whispered to me.

Let us not end this chapter on a sad note. Smiles are always better than tears, particularly in a hospice.

One patient whom we first met in his house then finally brought into the hospice was a local minister, renowned in evangelical circles. His GP chatted to me about him on the phone, telling me of his illness, how he hoped we might be able to help him and what other assistance he had in the house apart from his frail wife. I heard a faint chuckle, then he went on, 'Try to keep a straight face when you go in.' I asked him why.

'The place is full of texts. There're everywhere, on the doormat, on the walls, in the bathroom. Don't forget to wash your hands by the way when you've examined him!' I was intrigued.

It was exactly as he had described. On the doormat was not the usual 'Welcome' but 'Welcome to the House of the Lord'. Just as the doctor had warned me every square inch of wall seemed to be covered with texts from the Bible. However, I was not there to study texts but to see how we could make him more comfortable and soon I was unaware of the unusual surroundings, until I suggested that I go to the bathroom to wash my hands after examining him. As one does I took the opportunity to use the toilet.

There, prominently placed over the toilet so that neither I nor anyone else using it could be left in any doubt, was the text 'The Lord giveth and the Lord taketh away'.

When the time came for him to be admitted to the hospice he asked if he could bring in some of his personal treasures. Thankfully that text was not one of them.

Chapter VI

Waves of Anger

'A time to love and a time to hate.'

There is one word that crops up more frequently than most others in a hospice. You might expect it to be fear or faith, courage or certainty, suffering or pain. It is none of these, common as they are. It is anger. At some time or other everyone in a hospice seems to experience anger. The mystery and the wonder are that anger and safety, that other commonly used word, can and do co-exist. It is almost as if releasing anger creates safety.

How, you might ask, can there be anger in a place dedicated to peace, a place where pain is eased, families are reconciled and where love and compassion underpin everything?

The anger can be directed against anyone and everyone – against doctors for being unable to cure, for keeping them waiting, for explaining too much, for not listening, for being bad communicators, for not telling them everything, for telling them too much!

'I told him I wanted the truth, of course, but he didn't need to be as blunt as that!' or 'Surely there was a better way of telling Mum than asking her had she made a Will.'

Working in a hospice is one long learning experience especially when it comes to communications between patients and their doctors. Some illustrations might help to explain what I mean. Most patients read things into what a doctor says, things he or she never intended. Replying to that usually unanswerable question

'How long, doctor?' he might reply 'Well, I'm sure you are going to enjoy Christmas.' This is followed by an awful silence and a look of horror. 'So that's it then. I'm going to die in the week between Christmas and New Year.' When the doctor splutters that he never said that, and indeed never intended that interpretation the patient points out that if doctor had ever thought he would see the New Year he should have said so!

I well remember one summer being asked by a patient if I had any idea how long he had to live. As people always do he hastened to say that it was important for him to know though what he, or indeed anyone, would do with the information I do not know. I have yet to meet someone who then packs his bag and embarks on a round-the-world cruise like Sir Francis Chichester. I told him he had months and months, so far as I or anyone could judge. Far from being cheered he slumped down in his chair. 'Oh dear, I had so looked forward to having my last Christmas with the grandchildren.' I explained that that was still quite possible. 'Then why did you not say so instead of talking of months?'

A young man stood looking out of his bedroom window at the dusting of snow on the ground, the few snowdrops bringing the first hint of spring. 'Any idea how long I've got?' he asked me. As we often do, I asked him if he really wanted to know and did he appreciate how uncertain and inaccurate we doctors are when asked that question. Yes, he did. He was a scientist and jokingly said he knew doctors were not real scientists who worshipped accuracy.

'Well, I fully expect us both to be standing here, as we are doing now, and enjoying the daffodils when they appear.'

A few weeks later I found him standing in the same spot, tears silently trickling down his face. 'So the time has come then, doctor. Quite a thought!' I went and stood beside him and saw that the first daffodil had opened its trumpet just below his window. Spring came and went, as thousands of daffodils burst into colour and faded, long before he died.

We doctors do not make it easy for our patients and their loved ones. On most matters we cannot be precise, as scientists would be, but we do tend to be precise in our choice and use of words. The surgeon means well, but in fact leads to misunderstanding, when he says 'I managed to cut out all the tumour that I could see.' That is, of course, literally true but what he failed to say, and what the anxious patient might not have noticed, is that tumour could still be there but invisible to the naked eye.

Physicians can do the same when they have a patient sitting beside them and hold up an x-ray. It comes as such a relief to the patient, as it was intended to, to hear 'No sign of any tumour left on that x-ray.' What is not always appreciated by the anxious patient is that little tiny tumours are not visible to the naked eye on an simple x-ray yet are every bit as dangerous and ultimately life-threatening as the larger ones.

'Well I've got good news for you. I know that lump in your neck was worrying you after all you've gone through but I'm glad to say the biopsy of the gland did not show any cancer.' In all probability that is totally accurate, but what was not said was that the doctor already knew there was cancer *somewhere else*. All he has now said is that it was not found in the lump he has just had examined by the pathologist.

It is easy to understand how patients can feel deceived and aggrieved when they later find that their disease is not only still there but now threatening their life. 'I distinctly remember him saying he had taken it all away' or '. . . said he couldn't see it, he did.' Perhaps anger is too strong a word for the reactions but clearly there is disappointment, dismay, bewilderment, to say the least.

Before rushing either to condemn the medical profession or to condone bad communications it is perhaps important to emphasize that not all these examples are illustrations of bad or deceitful communications. Though most people *claim* that they want total honesty and truth from their doctors, experience shows that they do not usually want to be told everything about a malignant disease in its early days. They may want to know it is a cancer and they will most certainly want to know what are the treatment options and the success rate, but not much more than that. Relatives in particular are often very angry when a parent is told how serious an illness is even though the doctor has gone to considerable pains to outline all the treatment options and implications.

However, even this is an oversimplification. When people feel reasonably well they not only do not want to hear bad news. It is as if they often cannot absorb bad news. They cannot hear bad news even when they hear it. The corollary to that is that when someone is expecting bad news, they cannot hear any good news!

I recall many years ago sitting down beside a lady visiting a surgical clinic and explaining to her that the little tiny skin cancer we had removed from her hand was totally curable. It would not come back. It would not harm her. She was a very fortunate lady and we all felt very happy for her. Before that clinic finished her husband had arrived demanding to see me and threatening hellfire and damnation. How dare I tease his wife when she was now going to die! What sort of a doctor was I to laugh at a time like this! Why had I permitted her to go home when I knew she was dying? Perhaps the reader can understand what had happened. She was expecting to be told she had cancer and, as everyone seems to, she was certain her cancer would kill her. I used that word cancer when I spoke to her and suddenly it was as if her hearing failed. All she 'heard' was what she had come expecting to hear and not at all what I actually said. At least there was a happy ending to that tale.

We have all seen hundreds, or is it thousands, of people who swear blind that no doctor ever told them this or that but there it is, written in black and white in their case notes. Not only that, the notes detail the questions that patient asked and the answers that were given. Even recalling some of these examples is painful because at the centre of each story is a sad, disappointed person and a grieving family, once so protective but possibly now feeling foolish.

I recall one such as if it was yesterday. The husband was not just upset, he was furiously angry, that his wife was not going to get 'any more treatment', by which he meant that she would not receive any more radiotherapy or chemotherapy, not that she would not be exceedingly well looked after in the hospice. He was reminded that her cancer had spread to all organs of her body and that, sad as it was to have to say so, further attempts to cure it would be futile. He protested that, not only had he never been told this, in fact he had never once been spoken to by any doctor. His wife had been in a specialist cancer unit for several weeks but not a single doctor had made any effort to see him and explain anything, he told us. His anger was terrifying.

I phoned my colleagues in the cancer hospital and several of them vividly remembered speaking to him at different times, alone and with his wife. The consultant offered to come to the hospice immediately to help. He met the husband and stretched out his hand 'Good evening, sir. Nice to see you again. Do you remember me? I looked after your wife in the cancer hospital.'

'Of course I do, doctor. Good to see you again. I really enjoyed our talks.' When asked what the talks were about he had no recall whatsoever and to the day his wife died he never remembered any conversation about how ill she was or about her treatment. A unique case? No, sadly not. Some truth, some information is too painful to hear, too frightening to take on board. We either block it out or selectively remember the safer parts of the conversation. This selective memory loss is a well-recognized feature of bereavement but few people realize how common it is at other times of extreme stress. Put simply, some information is too painful, too threatening to be acceptable. The human brain seems to have a 'delete' button like a computer. No sooner is the unpleasant message received than it is deleted. Because something was said does not mean it was heard. Because something was heard does not mean it was understood. Why, oh why, do people talk about communication skills as if they were simple and straightforward!

Sometimes the anger or the resentment is directed against the health service for waiting lists, for delays, for lost letters, for wasted resources and so on. How can they spend so much on a computer or on redecorating the reception area and then turn round and say they have not sufficient left for an expensive drug? A good question it seems to me, but should we not all be asking how we could make better, more responsible use of the services? I suspect we have all been guilty of calling for ambulances when we do not need them, or of wasting drugs prescribed for us, or of failing to turn up for precious appointments, or of seeking medical help when self-medication would do equally well?

We seem to be living at a time when everyone knows their rights but cannot recall, or chooses not to remember, their responsibilities.

Particularly in cancer care there seems to be an assumption by the public that someone, somewhere, somehow, knows how to cure the cancer but their loved one's doctor certainly does not know. The problem is how to find that person. So much anger is vented because patient or relatives feel they are disadvantaged in having a doctor or a hospital which is not up-to-date. 'Why can't he phone America and ask what the best treatment is?' or, nearer to home 'Would anyone in London be able to help her?' I like to call this the Yellow Pages Syndrome. 'Of course I don't know who can do it but there must be someone in the book who can so let's find him.' Don't we all know from experience that sometimes even the Yellow Pages do not have all the miracle workers we find we need.

Sometimes the anger is directed at members of the family for their indifference, their failure to help Mum when she needs them, for not writing, for not caring, for not visiting, for being there too much, oh . . . for just being family!

Very, very often the anger is directed inwards to themselves. 'What a fool I've been! Smoking like that all my life' or 'Why was I so stubborn? I should have gone to the doctor months before.' 'Why did I not take earlier retirement when it was offered to me and I could have had some time with them all.' 'How I hate myself for being ill and bringing so much sadness into their lives.' One day a middle-aged man showed me an empty cigarette packet with its health warning clear for all to see. 'For the past two years, doctor, I've blamed the manufacturers for my lung cancer but I can't go on blaming them. I can read as well as anyone else,' he said, stabbing the health warning. 'I made the decision to smoke, not them, but it's so much easier to blame other people, isn't?'

Just occasionally the anger is directed at God but that after all, is a dangerous thing to do when you might meet Him in the not-too-distant future. Anything He has done well is ignored and scorn is heaped upon Him for not listening to our prayers, for favouritism, for behaving so badly towards his believers who, so they remind Him, have done a lot for Him. It should be noted, however, that people rarely speak directly to Him about how He has disappointed and failed them. Rather do they prefer to talk *about* Him in the hope He will overhear. The rare exception to that is when you are an old lady and God seems to have got your name mixed up with someone else's.

None of this may seem very important to the reader but to me there are two points worth making. The first is that being the punchbag on which someone is venting their fury can be painful, very painful indeed. Ask any hospice nurse or doctor about the stresses of their work and 'being at the receiving end of anger' will be cited. Both patients and relatives take the opportunity to offload their anger on whoever is nearest, and that is usually one of the professional care team. I have known half an hour or longer being spent as the captive audience, being told how everyone has failed, how nobody has been helpful or even honest, how God has gone down in their estimation and how they would change the health service, given the chance, then suddenly the verbal flood stopped dramatically.

'I hope you don't think I'm including you and the hospice in my criticism, doctor. I'll never have a bad word said about this place. Couldn't have been better! I just wish everywhere else had been like this place.' Then, the second point.

'It's a funny thing about the hospice, you know. You feel able to speak your mind here and say just how cross or upset you really are. I've never felt that anywhere else. It's a good feeling. I feel so much happier now that I've got everything off my chest.' Hospice care does not *produce* anger but it acts as a safety valve releasing anger, anger which left inside would eventually erupt and make their dying even worse.

Is that something else we have learned? There is, I believe, some anger in most of us. Leave it inside and it bubbles and bubbles until it comes to the boil. On the other hand, letting it out in a controlled manner seems to be therapeutic; what psychologists might term cathartic. Does it need a psychologist to do it? Apparently not but it does have to be asked if helping people, as hospices try to do, needs to be so traumatic and bruising. It does seem to be reminding us yet again that a 'safe' environment is one where people can be themselves, can express their feelings, and come through the experience better and healthier than when they went in.

However, it is worth remembering that a safe environment for the patient may be a bruising environment for some of the carers. Why do most people only find such a safe environment at the end of life instead of throughout it, I wonder? How many grieving relatives know how battered hospice nurses and doctors can feel at the end of a typical day?

Is there something here worth exploring? Hospices are very ordinary places, staffed by very ordinary professionals, looking after ordinary people coming towards the end of life, yet many of the things described in this little book are quite extraordinary. I am thinking of the sense of freedom to express anger and not be rebuked or disciplined for doing so. I am remembering the changes that have taken place in people; the cantankerous old man who returns to being someone who is a delight to know, the shy one who 'comes out of his shell' and is everyone's helper, the selfish one who suddenly cannot do enough for others and expects no thanks. A colleague once remarked that patients in a hospice often experience the Hyde and Jekyll Syndrome. With infinite patience I pointed out that the Syndrome was actually called Jekyll and Hyde, the good man turning into the unpleasant who is in us all. No, he said, he had not made a mistake. The remarkable thing is that the nearer people get to death the nicer they become. He was right. That, after all, was one of the things that made this work so memorable and so worthwhile.

How could I forget the first man who told me that his three weeks in the hospice had been the happiest in his life? What does this say about his life rather than about the hospice? If he had been unique in this comment we might have ignored it but many others have said the same. Had they never known happiness or had it taken a different shape? Had they perhaps spent their lives looking for it rather than trying to give it?

What did the ex-convict mean when he said he had never been so well cared for before – that our ambience and facilities were superior to HM Prisons? I hope they were but he clearly meant something else and explained it to us. 'You all know about my past but somehow I don't have to explain or apologize here and I don't have to pretend to be what I'm not!'

Has he hit the nail on the head? I believe he has. He found himself accepted unconditionally and did not need to pretend, or to act, as if he was anyone but himself. That, it seems to me, is at the heart of hospice and palliative care. That is the 'secret' which, if it underpinned everyday living rather than just our dying, could make our world a better place. There were no doubts about this when you talked to the patients, and many of their families.

'Having money for everything I wanted and always creating the right impression were all that mattered to me before I came in here. Now they seem so unimportant.'

Said another, 'If you'd asked me a few years ago I would have insisted on being in a single room, and not having to share with any old Tom, Dick or Harry, but now there's nothing I enjoy more than being with the other men even though we're all very different. You see the things we have in common are so much more important than the old school tie stuff of the past, keeping up appearances and pretending to be a better person, or a cleverer person, than I really am.'

Another man chipped in. 'Where I was brought up you had to fight for everything. If you didn't you got nothing. So I've spent my life fighting – my wife, my mates, the police – everyone and everything. I came along here and found that I got what I needed, and more, without fighting, without playing the tough lad. I didn't need to raise my voice or thump the table.'

'You ask is there anything I would like, doctor? Oh yes. A chance to live my life again using all that I've seen and learnt in here.'

Perhaps the most poignant quote of all. 'Sad? You ask if I'm sad! Of course I'm sad. Wouldn't you be sad if it had taken you all your life, right up to the time when you're due to die, to find out what life is all about?'

Well, at least he discovered it. Many people never do!

Chapter VII

The Truth, the Whole Truth . . .

'The truth shall make you free.' St John's Gospel

Doctors spend five or six years at university before qualifying, then as many again (if not more) training to become specialists. In that time they are expected to acquire a vast amount of theoretical knowledge, considerable practical experience and even a modicum of wisdom. Most of their teachers and exemplars are fellow doctors and surgeons. It is only as they get older that they realize, however, that their most influential teachers were probably not these eminent men and women but their patients, their nursing colleagues and, sometimes, their young students. I recall, more years ago than I care to mention, starting my first job after qualifying. The distinguished surgeon who had had the courage to accept me as one of his juniors welcomed me and took me to meet the person he described as 'your teacher for the next six months'. It was the ward sister. She did indeed teach me, at times making me feel less daunted by the surgeon than by her, and what she taught has served me well all my professional life.

My first lesson on fear was given by just such a nurse, a ward sister in charge of an acute medical ward but she would have been equally good wherever she worked. My experience was severely limited, two days to be precise. I had graduated a few weeks before, had a lovely holiday then started work as a locum in a famous teaching hospital. I had been there less than two days, the longest days in my life. It was a Sunday afternoon and I was called to see a lady who looked to me as though she might die of her asthma, a tragic but not altogether rare event in those far-off days. I gave her the necessary injection and sat by her bedside in case she needed another injection. I had been led to believe in those all-so-recent student days that within minutes the patient would be better and, hopefully, very appreciative of what the doctor had done, young-looking as I was. It surprised me that this lady was not yet able to do that.

Sister came and whispered in my ear that my tea had been poured out and was getting cold. I was shocked. How could anyone be so insensitive and uncaring? Could she not see that I was busy saving this lady's life? The asthma seemed to get worse and I hovered over her, massive loaded syringe poised to strike. 'Come and get your tea, doctor.' I might only have been working as a doctor for two days but I knew how to give her a look of rebuke. I suspect it was the first time I had realized how uncaring some people can be!

'May I have a quick word with you, doctor?' I turned away from the patient as Sister whispered to me. 'Forgive me saying so, doctor, but your anxiety is making her worse. If you come and have your tea and a little cake I have left for you I'll keep an eye on her from a distance and I think you'll find she'll settle well.' I had my doubts but there was something in the way she said it that left me in no doubt that I was not being given a choice, a little bit like a patient being asked would he like an enema.

Five minutes later I looked through the office window and there was the patient sitting up in bed singing hymns for the ward service! 'You see, doctor,' said Sister 'fear breeds fear and fear makes everything that much worse to bear. You had fear written all over your face as you sat there! Frankly you looked more frightened than the patient did!' Of course, she was right. I realized how observant she was when she asked had I enjoyed the second cake, hers, as much as the first one she had left for me!

Many years later a student stayed behind after a lecture I had given on the fears experienced by people coming to the end of life, and said that it seemed to him that 'the antidote to fear seems to be truth.'

How obvious, how simple and how true but I had never heard it articulated in that way. Fear breeds on fear, as Sister had taught me, and on ignorance or insufficient knowledge. Give truthful, accurate information and, so his argument went, there should be less fear. I believe he was right, certainly as far as the fears of the dying are concerned. The challenge seems to be to create the right 'safe' ambience and to learn how to give just sufficient information for the person's needs. Too little information allows their minds to fill the voids with all sorts of terrors. Too much information can suffocate them.

Giving critically important information to a patient is, it seems to me, very like giving an injection. It can be given all at once, like the emergency injections we give straight into the blood stream, the whole dose going into the patient within minutes. It can be given slowly, over days or weeks, gently and carefully, like the 'drips' you see in hospitals, in such measured tiny amounts that the patient is scarcely aware of receiving them. The first type is rarely called for and can be a dreadful shock to the 'system', whereas the slow drip achieves equally good results and is slow enough to give the system time to cope with it, get used to it and adapt.

As an example a doctor might tell a patient that he has cancer, that it is an incurable one, that he is almost certain to suffer pain and that he will die in the not too distant future. All true, no doubt, but what doctor would ever speak like that to a patient and which patient would ever want their doctor to subject them to such a torrent of bad news? The answer is that a surprising number of people say they want to be told 'everything' ('Give it to me straight, doctor') and, in response to that, there are even some doctors who do so, with catastrophic effects. ('Well, don't blame me. He said he wanted to be told everything.')

Among the myths which have grown up around hospice and palliative care are that its doctors and nurses expect their patients to know everything about their condition, and, secondly, that they expect them to talk about it all the time and actually feel better for doing so! It is also widely believed that if someone goes into a hospice or palliative care unit and has not already been told everything about the illness, including its grim outcome, they will there and then be informed, not by the slow kindly drip method but by the single dramatic shot, whether they want it or not, whether it will help them or harm them.

Nothing could be farther from the truth. I recall a hospice nursing director saying that she could not remember talking to any patients about either death or dying in the previous three months. There was no need to. They knew all they wanted to know and if they ever had more questions they knew whom to ask. It is perhaps important to remember that not only had she not needed to speak of death and dying but neither would she have denied them, or offered false hope, if anyone had asked her. It is also a timely reminder that even dying people prefer to speak about life rather than about death and dying.

The important thing, as hundreds of patients confirmed, is that they should have all the information *they* feel they need, at the time *they* feel the need for it and not as and when their doctors and relatives dictate. They know what they are frightened about, far better than anyone else. They know their own limitations but, curiously, seldom appreciate how great are their strengths. Perhaps a little story will illustrate a dilemma faced by the terminally ill. I suspect that it is relevant not only to the dying but to most of us at different times throughout life.

The patient was an ex-Marine Commando, as tough and macho as any man you could meet. Listening to him recount his experiences of life and death in deserts and jungles made you wonder if he knew the meaning of fear as the rest of us do. When I once asked him did he know what it was like to be frightened he laughed and said he had been terrified more times than he could number, then added 'and I can tell you precisely what terrifies me. It is the unknown. I have never once been frightened when I knew who the enemy was, what he looked like, where he was, what he might do to us, what weapons he had at his disposal. Never once, even when the odds were all against us! What always frightened me to death was fighting in the dark at night. All we were told was that he was out there somewhere but where? God knows.

'We used to ask everything we could about the enemy before we went out on a mission. How many were there? What sort of weapons did they have? How were they likely to attack us? What could we expect – you know the sort of thing?

'When you are fighting in total darkness, no matter how well trained you are and how good your weapons, every sound scares you. Who made it? Where did it come from? Are they in front of you or behind you? When nothing happens you don't relax – you just get more scared wondering where the next sound will come from, the next crackle of a twig. What was that sound? Was it someone's breathing? Was that the squeal of an animal? The more you thought about it the more convinced you became that it was someone's breathing and any minute you might have an arm round your neck and a knife about to slash your throat open.

'Give me an enemy I can see, any day. What terrifies me here, even here in the hospice, and what has always scared me, is the unknown, doctor. Honest, I'm not really too scared of cancer or of death even though it's coming too soon, but of what *might* happen, what I *might* have to suffer – that's why I'm always asking you questions. Why am I getting this pain here? Why did I have that nightmare last night? I need to know what to expect.'

He looked at me to see if I was listening and smiled when he found that he had a small audience. Not only I was captivated by his life's experiences, in one way so different from mine yet in another so typical of what we all go through at some time or other.

'Do you see what I'm getting at, doctor? Do you understand

what I'm trying to tell you? I can pluck up a wee bit of courage when I have to but I must know why I'll need it. If you can tell me that I'll get a bit of pain here or here, or that I might not sleep at night or that I might hallucinate (or whatever you docs call it) then I'm OK. What scares the s*** out of me is a niggle that I didn't expect. What does it mean? Is that a lump of cancer getting bigger? Is my leg going to go black and fall off? I wake up in the morning and feel muddled and confused. Oh God help me. What's happening? Am I going mad? Will I lose my mind before I die? Why do I feel sick this morning? Is the cancer in my stomach now? Why is this happening? How many times can I ask the doctors and nurses silly questions before they get fed-up with me?'

One of the other patients spoke up. He was well educated with an accent which confirmed a privileged background. 'My problem was that, way back when my cancer was first found, I told them I wanted to know everything. I meant it, of course, or I wouldn't have said it but they told me so much that I couldn't take most of it in and what little I did remember I got all muddled. If I had the chance again I would ask to be told just a little bit and tell them that I'll come back for more when I'm ready – a bit like a good meal, if you ask me. Small helpings but there's always more if you want to come back. You get less indigestion that way!'

The ex-marine looked around at us and asked if he could finish with just one more tale. He needn't have asked.

'My worst ever experience was in a jungle in the Far East fighting a guerrilla army. Pitch dark, dripping humidity, leeches all over you and out there somewhere, God knows where, a bunch of killers who knew the jungle like the back of their hands. We knew some were on the ground but we also knew that many were in underground tunnels and could come up to the surface almost anywhere. We each knew that at any moment they could pounce on us and slit our throats. Don't anyone believe that a jungle is a quiet place, even in the black of night – it is noisy, I can tell you. There were sounds all around us – a twig here, an animal disturbed over there, a frog to your right and something you couldn't identify to your left. We were soon convinced the bandit group was at least twenty or thirty in number and we were surrounded by them, Not for one minute did I take my finger off the trigger. For hour after hour I listened to a steady thumping sound – my own heart thumping away in terror. Sweat poured out all night. Every few minutes there would be a blood-curdling scream from a monkey being trapped by some predator but for all I knew it could have been one of my mates having his throat slit. It was the longest night of our lives, packed with terror from start to finish – and all because we could not see him and knew next-to-nothing about the enemy. When morning came and the first shafts of light broke through the canopy we learned that the guerrilla group had never been near us! They had moved on the previous day. We had been alone all night. Alone with fear.'

'You are so right' said one of the men. 'It is the unknown which terrifies us all.'

That perfectly describes what we have learned in hospice care. Fears breeds on ignorance. Most patients fear things which are not likely to happen, because no-one has taken the time to explain things slowly and simply. Understandably there are more things about their illness that they do *not* know than there are that they *do* know. This creates more and more fear. It seems to be like a building whose foundation is faulty. No matter how many bricks you lay on it and how well they are laid that building is unsafe because of the foundation. If in the beginning a patient is given false information, half truths or deliberate untruths then whatever is explained to them after that may not help because the foundation of their knowledge and information is suspect. People do not only need truth at the end of their life but throughout it. It is no different from what our parents taught us and we have tried to inculcate in our own children, namely that when you once tell a lie you have to go on doing so.

One day we admitted a lady from our Home Care Service. I had been reminded by my colleagues that her mother had died in the hospice a few years before so we made every effort not to have her in the same room with all its memories. How sad, I thought to myself, to sit by your mother's bedside and see her go then to have to come in yourself as a patient. I wondered what she thought of the place, whether she had good memories, and how she would react. As soon as possible after she was settled in and enjoying a cup of tea and some home-made Scots shortbread I went along to welcome her. I had not expected what followed. People usually put on a brave smile but it is obvious that they are frightened and very ill at ease, with good reason. This lady was different.

'Oh doctor. I cannot tell you how happy I am to be here. I feel safe at last.' With that she laughingly flopped back on to her pillows as most of us do when trying out the bed in the hotel or holiday home as soon as we arrive.

I told her that of course I was delighted she felt so welcome and indeed so safe but how could she feel that when the hospice must hold many sad memories for her.

'I'm so relieved no longer to be under the care of my GP because he is the world's best liar, believe me. I've never known what, if anything, I could believe when he spoke to me but here – I know I can always trust everybody to be honest with me. That's why.'

Now, I knew her GP very well and had the highest opinion of him. I would have been delighted to put myself and my family in his hands. There was no way I could let her get away with calling him a liar like that. 'I know your doctor very well and I have to say that calling him the world's best liar is grossly unfair, if you don't mind me saying so.'

'Doctor, do you remember my mother had cancer and died under your care? From the day I was told about her cancer by that same GP I made it my responsibility to see that she would never learn the diagnosis, never hear what it was either from the doctor or from any of her family. I went to the doctor and made myself quite clear on the matter. I admit he wasn't exactly happy about it but agreed under a little pressure from me. I told him what to say, how to answer her questions, how to keep her in the dark. Give him credit, he was so good that, so far as I'm aware, she died never once suspecting there was anything serious.' She fell silent as she looked at me, as if gathering strength for what was to come. I wondered if she was going to ask me to confirm that her mother had indeed died unaware of how ill she was but if she did I had a problem. We had looked up her case notes and there it said she had deduced the diagnosis and asked us to confirm it because no-one else would do so!

'When I myself became unwell and went to see him he at first seemed to be quite open and frank. He's very charming, as you know. As time passed and I had more and more tests then went to him for the results, he seemed to change. I felt I couldn't trust him. Whatever he said, I kept wondering if it was him speaking or was he just mouthing something my husband or family had told him to say, the way I had done with mother. When mother was ill and I needed a good liar he was the best I could ever hope to find. When it came my turn, the last thing I wanted was to be looked after by such a skilled liar. I wanted truth and I don't know to this day if I've ever had it from him. Now do you understand?

'He'd say things like, "You don't need to worry about this or that," and I didn't know whether to believe him or not. He said I'd have no pain, but how could I be sure? I kept asking my husband if they'd come to some agreement about what I was or was not to be told and, as you can imagine he got angry with me but still the thought that he was lying niggled at the back of my mind. If he could lie to protect Mum why couldn't he do the same for me?'

The truth can be painful but it can also help you to feel *safe*. What a surprising word to use, but nevertheless the commonest word people ever use when describing their time in a hospice. What does this tell us about our everyday world and its hypocrisies, its empty boastings and promises, its shallowness. That people can be in a place of death and yet feel safe must surely teach us something.

One day our nurses asked me to set time aside to help a patient who had come into the hospice two weeks before, paralysed from the waist down from cancer which had spread to his spine, sadly a not uncommon event. The specialist surgical team who had referred him made a point of telling us that he knew everything about his condition, and, in particular, that he would never walk again. As each day passed he became more depressed and withdrawn, very different from the 'life and soul of the party' man his friends described. I asked him if he would like to talk to me or ask me anything which might possibly help him.

'I want you to know I've never been better looked after in my life, doctor. Nobody could ever complain about this place – the nurses, the food, the comforts – it's a wonderful place. What's getting me down is the thought that I'm to be here for the next, oh I don't know, fifteen or twenty years stuck in this b***** wheelchair, useless, not even able to help the other blokes.'

I asked him how much he knew and understood about his illness. What had he been told, or perhaps more correctly, what had he understood of the things explained in his previous hospital.

'Cannot complain about there either, doctor. They gave it to me straight, no messing about! The specialist sat down beside me and told me I had an incurable disease in my spine and that I would never walk again. He put his hand on my wheelchair and said I'd be in it for the rest of my life. Can't speak plainer than that I'd have thought.'

The problem was obvious. I had the choice of leaving him in the dark about the true nature of his illness or breaking what most people would have described as 'bad news' to him. Clearly he was unprepared but equally he was getting more despondent by the day. I told him that I totally agreed with everything he had been told. However, I was surprised he had not asked, nor had he been told, what the disease in his spine was. Did he want to know, I asked him.

'Of course I want to know, doctor. It can't be worse than being told you'll never walk again.'

'You have cancer which has spread to your spine, spread there from your prostate.'

There was a moment of silence then slowly, ever so slowly a smile crossed his face. Still nothing was said but the smile grew wider and wider until he was positively beaming. The only word which could describe it would be delighted. He grasped my hand and began to shake it as if we had met after a lifetime of separation.

'That's the best news I've ever had in my life, doctor. So it won't be fifteen years, or even ten or even five, I suppose. What about five months?' I shook my head.

'Less than five months stuck in this wheelchair and you'll let me stay here? Wonderful! I suppose you think I'm mad but you know, by the time you get to my age it isn't death that frightens you but the sort of life you're going to have to endure before you die. Death doesn't frighten me but how I die certainly does. Funny that, isn't it? Fancy anyone saying they're not really scared of dying. Never thought I'd ever say that!'

I can almost hear the murmuring grunts of disapproval of some shocked readers. 'Fancy taking away hope! Everyone needs hope and all you seem to be talking about is removing hope with all this talk of honesty, telling people they are going to die or at least confirming that. Man needs hope to survive and you seem intent on shattering what little hope your patients ever had.'

Thank you for bringing that up. It is a matter of the greatest possible importance. It forces us to ask what we mean by hope. Is it a fanciful dream, a fantasy, something unrelated to reality? Does hope always mean a return to happiness and health? Even that is more difficult to answer than might at first appear for what is health? Freedom from disease or balanced wholeness of body, mind and spirit? We could go on asking these existential questions for a long time but might it not be better to ask our patients what *they* mean by hope? A few of their quotes might surprise the reader as much as we were all surprised when we did this.

'I used to hope for a cure until it became obvious that that was looking for a miracle and I don't believe in them. So, what I hope for now is that I shan't suffer pain, that people won't patronize me in what they say and how they say it, and that everyone will be honest with me. The iller I get the less I can tolerate lies, no matter how well-intentioned.'

'Do I still hope? You bet I do! I hope people will listen to me. I hope that people will be open with me and stop treating me like a kid.'

'Yes, I still have a lot of hope but not for miracle cures, if that's what you mean. What I'm hoping for is a little longer with my wife and children, without the pain that nearly killed me.'

'I have as much hope in me as I have ever had but it's different hope. It's not about cures and getting well again but about how people relate to me. I hope I have enough time left to meet people who really care, to meet people who know the meaning of truth and decency. I hope that I can bring hope to someone else.'

'You're asking if I have any hope left. Is that what you want to know? Well, don't laugh but my greatest hope is that there is something after all this, after I've gone, whether you call it heaven or not doesn't matter. Until I got this cancer I didn't give a damn about those things. I just lived for each day. Now I feel I've learnt so much I'd like a chance to use it so let's hope there's another life.' The speaker was a man who could keep a straight face only for a few minutes before he would make a joke and this time was no exception. 'I might just come back as a cat and scare the old lady – she hates them!'

The reasons for hospice and palliative care could hardly have been better articulated. The aim is to restore *quality* of life even when, to put in rather crudely, the *quantity* of life cannot be changed.

It looks as though to achieve that we need to provide two essential ingredients, honesty and integrity, but they often seem to be in short supply in our modern world. How sad that some people have to get to the end of their lives before they experience them, but how fascinating that when they do encounter them, they recognize them at once. We seem to be able to home in on them as if we have built-in receivers. This deserves more thought.

Chapter VIII

People Know

'A time to be born and a time to die.'

How is it that some people seem to know when they are about to die? I think we must also ask how it is that a few people, even when desperately ill, know they are *not* just about to die, even when all around them, including the doctors, are expecting it any day.

What a macabre subject, you might say but I suggest it is important. I was first alerted to this phenomenon of knowing when death would occur when working with an African tribe many years ago. Most of the patients suffered from tuberculosis and inevitably the death rate was appallingly high. The hospital, though well equipped with almost everything it needed, was in a remote rural area, the people were for the most part uneducated and totally unsophisticated, and modern medicine as we practise it in the West was a very new experience to them. They came late, the disease already far-advanced, and had neither time nor inclination to remain in the hospital until their lengthy treatment had rendered them fit for home again, not cured but less infectious.

Superstition was rife. They knew for a certainty their illness was because some enemy had put a spell on them. The worse the spell, the more certainly they would die whether they deserved it or not. This condition of coughing, wasting, sweating was nothing to do with those little invisible enemies the white doctor spoke about and which he said he could see down that tube with the bright light at the bottom. They knew what the white doctor did not know, that they had had spells put on them and some of those spells were actually powerful enough to kill. The white doctor gave you pills and potions (incidentally not very powerful because they did not taste awful) and for minor spells they seemed to work reasonably effectively. Every now and then, however, a killing spell or curse was put on someone and . . .!

All this was quite new to me. For some reason all mention of this aspect of care had been omitted from my undergraduate and postgraduate training, My *real life* training began one day when I was doing rounds in the male tuberculosis wards. One of the patients who had come in so ill that no-one, not least the man himself, ever thought he would go home again, was now strong enough to be discharged. His latest x-rays showed an excellent response to his anti-tuberculosis therapy; his blood tests were equally good and his appetite and energy had both returned. All-in-all an excellent response, a real credit to western medicine, as I pointed out to all the sceptics around me.

Not that many would have believed me if they had seen him that day. He was curled up in bed, the picture of abject misery. He had turned his back on all the other patients and was reluctant even to look at me. I thought the best thing was to tell him the good news, that he could go home next day.

'I'm not going home.' I looked around at the nurses but nobody knew any more than I did. 'I shall be dead before the sun bleeds into that hill tonight.' I was sensitive enough not to laugh at him even though I wanted to but, to my horror everyone else took it seriously.

'Shall I call in the next person from the waiting list?' asked Sister, herself an African. I was relieved that she at least was being sensible because there would be a vacant bed after he had gone home but, to my alarm, she went on. 'Shall I get them in after sunset tonight or tomorrow morning?'

To my utter dismay everyone believed he would die that night and was terror-stricken. They were awe-struck that such a powerful curse had been put on him. Being a well trained western doctor with no time for such superstitions I decided to sit beside him at sunset to demonstrate how groundless were his fears.

He died exactly as he had foretold. Exactly as the sun set behind the hills he died. I carried out a post-mortem and found no cause whatsoever for his sudden death.

It would be reassuring if I could report that this was a unique case, a one-off. It was not. Rather was it one of many and every time I heard that it was going to happen the patient was submitted to the most thorough examination and even put on to cardiac monitors as in an intensive care unit. The death always occurred when and where the patient said it would.

However, you might say, that was primitive Africa and we are talking about a modern hospice in a world famous university city. Let me tell you the story of a charming and very gracious lady in that hospice.

This lady had been admitted 'fighting for breath' as they say, and in her case that was literally true. In addition to her cancer she had a chronic lung disease and so impaired was her breathing that she had not been out of her flat for close on two years when Sister and I visited her at home. She must often have felt like a prisoner but no-one had ever heard her complain. Her flat was a show piece, with nothing out of place, everything matching in colour and style and with a glorious view across the city rooftops. As the cancer grew so her breathlessness got worse and when she contracted a chest infection that was the last straw. She needed little persuasion that she should come in to the hospice. She needed oxygen in the ambulance and could scarcely speak to us for a few days. Can anything be more frightening than being unable to get your breath? I suspect not.

With what little breath she had she asked me 'Is this it?' and I had to say I suspected it was, but one of us would always be beside her, day and night, and if the sheer terror became more than anyone could manage I was prepared to tranquillize her without actually shortening her life. Her little family understood and, if one can ever say such a thing, accepted the situation. To our surprise and our delight, she improved dramatically until she was able to sit out of bed. Within another few days she was enjoying her evening tipple of sherry before a light meal. Needless to say her sherry was 'purely medicinal, doctor.'

One evening just before 7 o'clock I went into her room to bid her goodnight before I went off duty. She looked a different lady from the one who had been brought in to us in such distress and fear. He colour was good, her breathing much better and judging by what she was eating her appetite was better. Putting down her glass she asked me what time I would be back in the hospice next morning. When told it would be shortly after 8 o'clock she took my hand and thanked me for all I had done for her saying 'Sorry I shan't have you here, but you do know how grateful I am, don't you?'

I am ashamed to say I was short with her. 'Why are you talking like this? I'll see you in the morning and in the meantime I hope you have a very comfortable night.'

'You don't seem to understand what I am trying to tell you, doctor. I shall be dead before you come back, unless you change your mind and come on duty by 7 o'clock!'

'Now let's have no more of this depressed talk. I could have understood you speaking like this when you first came in, if you'd had the breath to do so, but you're so much better that in a few days we'll start making arrangements to get you home.' With that I prepared to leave her, but she called me back.

'Doctor dear, you are a clever man but you don't know my body as well as I do. I know what's happening to it, you know. Good night and thank you again.'

When I went in to my office next morning there on the desk was a note to say she had died just before 7 o'clock. How was it that she knew that night but had not known when she was admitted?

No one seems able to describe what it is they feel which makes them so certain that death is imminent. What they all say, however, is that the experience is not frightening in any way. They speak of feeling 'different from any other time I remember' and sensing that there is nothing left to do or to finish. With experience doctors and nurses in hospices learn to ask questions about what ambitions are still unfulfilled, what work there is still to do, what milestones remain. So long as a person can still identify something they are looking forward to there is still life ahead for them. When they cannot think of anything, death is probably imminent. What is important to note is that to the observer there may seem to be many reasons for them going on living but what seems to matter is what the patient feels.

One lady, as ill as any I had ever seen, came into our care with widespread cancer of the ovary. Both she and her husband knew well how ill she was. As he sat beside her watching me examining her and then sitting down beside them for a chat, he looked up and said, almost as if he was lessening the burden for me 'It's a matter of days then, doctor?' I nodded gently for words seemed superfluous.

'What *are* you talking about, Charles? Baby's not due for three weeks!' He looked at her with a mixture of love and bewilderment then up at me. 'Our first grandchild, doctor.'

Three weeks later that lady was not only alive; she was at home waiting to see the little one for the first time. There are some occasions which no words can describe. This was one. Frail and wasted, she somehow managed to stand as the car drew up and, without any assistance, walked to the door to see her first grandchild. I visited her that evening at the invitation of her family doctor.

'So that was what you were living for! How wonderful for you all. And now?' Of course I expected her to admit that she was exhausted and ready to die now that her final dream had been fulfilled. How wrong I was.

'Now it's time for Charles and I to celebrate our wedding anniversary in a few weeks time. I intend it to be quite a party so I hope you'll come along, doctor.' Husband Charles said nothing but just looked at me, his eyebrows raised, his eyes looking heavenward.

The party was indeed a success, if a very emotional one. A day or two later I saw her again and intended to ask what the next goal was that she was aiming for. She forestalled me.

'Well, doctor, time to go. This is it! Don't ask me how I know but I feel it in my bones.'

'There must be more things to look forward to, aren't there – things like birthdays, baby's christening and so on. Aren't you going to keep yourself alive for a few more weeks the way you did for baby's arrival and your anniversary?'

'I can't explain, doctor. It just feels different. I am not depressed or morbid in any way, though I don't mind admitting I'm a bit disappointed I'm not going to see the little one grow up. I just know my time has come.' She was right. She died next day.

I have mentioned elsewhere the distinguished professor of law who was so frail that one wondered how he kept going but there, on the floor of his flat, were literally hundreds of pages of the encyclopaedia he was editing. After I had examined him he asked me 'the score' as he put it. 'I should finish this in a few weeks so how much time do you think I have after that to get the comments of my colleagues around the world?'

I began, as gently as possible, to say that time was probably very much shorter than he had imagined and I greatly feared he might not get his *magnum opus* finished. I shall never forget his response.

'Stupid of me to ask you, wasn't it? How should *you* know? After all it's my body and I should just go by what it tells me . . . that is if I ever get a chance to listen to it with all this work to finish. I'm pretty sure I've got longer than you quacks imagine! The problem will be when I have no more work to do on this thing.'

How right he was. He died a few weeks after finishing it. Is it not curious how people have goals or targets which they know of but which they may never have mentioned to others. They achieve them and then die as if the motor stops for some reason. Should we ask more people what they are living for? I think we probably should. After all, it is the most important thing in their life at that point.

We once had a devout Catholic patient whose priest came in regularly to see him. I met him after one visit and he stopped in the corridor and whispered that he suspected his friend would not see another day but it did not matter because he was ready to go. Later in the morning I had a word with him and asked if he really was as ready as the priest had said to me, in a sense just waiting for 'the call', as he always termed it.

'Oh no. I've one final goal and after that I'll be away.' I asked what that was but he just laughed and said 'You'll soon find out.'

A few days later the new Archbishop was being taken round and he stopped at the bedside as he did with every patient. He was a natural sick-visitor with a ready and appropriate word for everyone, a truly gifted pastor. My patient obviously enjoyed the visit and as the Archbishop left the room the patient winked at me and whispered, 'That was it.'

A few minutes later after seeing the Archbishop off I was met by a nurse telling me that my patient had died. You cannot get better timing than that, I would have thought.

I once recounted similar stories to a friend who was a veterinary surgeon. He was not in the least surprised because, as he explained, animals seem to know when they need rest and when they are going to die. They detach themselves from the pack or the herd and go off alone, without food or water, and curl up and die. 'I bet you wish more of your patients were as sensible and easy to look after as my animals!' It was meant as a joke, and I took it as that (though I was tempted to say I wish I earned as much as he did), but in fact his remark contained much wisdom. One of the thoughts that keeps coming back to you working in a hospice is how sophisticated, how blasé, we have become in our modern society. Dare I add that we have also become more than enthusiastic about the scientific, we have become obsessed with it?

This is dangerous talk for a physician, so perhaps a few words of explanation would be in order so that I am not called before the Inquisition as a heretic.

Not for one minute am I decrying modern medicine or scientific advances. What has happened this century, and in particular in the second half of it, has been truly amazing. I feel more privileged than words can describe to have worked at the time we first had antibiotics, anti-cancer drugs, radiotherapy, 'keyhole' and transplantation surgery and truly incredible advances in our knowledge and applications of genetics, to say nothing of the diagnostic wonders of x-rays, scanning and magnetic resonance imaging (MRI).

It is the unexpected sequels to this veritable scientific tidal wave which trouble me. Not only have many doctors come to feel that science has all the answers; so have many members of the public, the patients they serve. The scientific approach has much to commend it. What can be measured *is* measured; where a cause can be identified which will explain a known result, we have reasons to be pleased. Where an experiment or test or procedure can be replicated getting the same predictable result, we have good reason to be pleased. This is science in all its glory. What we must not do is to expect *everything* to be measurable or reproducible; not must we expect that a cause will always be found to satisfy our craving for 'cause and effect' in illness and in health. Life and death are simply not like that.

Time after time, day after day in the hospice (or any hospital, come to that) loving relatives press doctors to incriminate something, or even someone, for the mortal illness of their loved ones. This is understandable and logical if, armed with the facts, they then changed their own life style and habits to prevent themselves falling victim to cancer, but that did not happen. Was it his job? Was it the food? Was it the strain of his work or what happened when he was in the Army or a prisoner of war camp? In recent years the questions have tended to focus on the professionals and the Health Service into whose hands the patient had placed himself. If 'they' had got it sooner would it have made any difference? The operation should have been done much earlier, shouldn't it? Would this ever have happened if the surgeon had been more experienced?

So eager are people to have explanations, or to find scapegoats, that they find it well-nigh impossible to accept that complex diseases like cancer have complex and multiple causes so far as we know. They seek high and low for something or someone to blame and often continue to smoke like chimneys as they do so! How well I remember a young son grieving the death of a much-loved dad. He stood with me at the door of the hospice, because relatives were not permitted to smoke inside, puffing away at his cigarette and saying 'Oh doctor, how often we tried to tell him that cigarettes would be the death of him but would he listen? No! What a fool my dad was!' On another occasion I was invited by a family to visit them in the evening their mother died, and to see her in her coffin in the living room. The plan was that after I had seen her and paid my respects the lid would be put on. That was duly done and then, to my horror, they all lit up, filling the small room with acrid smoke and using the coffin lid as a resting place for the ashtrays. 'Doctor, when will you doctors find a cause for lung cancer like Mum's?' they all wanted to know.

Perhaps I see my own profession through the faintly rose coloured spectacles of old age and am less critical of colleagues and myself than I once was. I seem to meet more and more doctors who are discovering and being fascinated by some of the mysteries of our art, rather than the intricacies of our craft, paradoxical as that sounds. They no longer scoff when someone speaks of 'the bedside manner' as if it had been replaced by blood tests. Like me, they have noticed that where we stand, how we speak and how we show that we care is probably every bit as important to the patient as the latest blood results. Many colleagues now share my fascination with the power of what I would call 'controlled silence'. There are times when the best prescription is quiet listening, resisting the temptation to speak all the time, and letting empathetic silence say it all.

One of the exercises we used to give the senior medical students who came to learn at the hospice was to sit for ten minutes listening to a patient, but forbidden to say anything except a courteous grunt. They were asked to introduce themselves to the patient (who had of course been spoken to and agreed in advance) and then to sit looking at the patient but saying nothing other than an acknowledgement by way of a nod or the grunt I have mentioned. Easy? More difficult and challenging than any of them expected and, incidentally, a completely new experience for most of them. At the de-briefing afterwards, over a cup of coffee, they used to describe how impatient they had felt, how eager to ask further questions or to interrupt the patient's flow of words – just typical doctors, you might say. As one student said, so honestly and so humbly, 'I've never listened so carefully before and, you know, it was really interesting. I'll do that again.'

In a world of such scientific advances and medical discoveries as we have outlined, it is tempting for a doctor to feel that miracles are possible though likely to be time-consuming, and that answers can be provided for everything if we are sufficiently knowledgeable and skilled. It is tempting but it is also wrong, just as it is wrong and likely to lead to much disappointment and sadness when our patients have unrealistic expectations. It took a hospice to teach me that it is safe even for a consultant physician to say, not once but many hundreds of times, 'I don't have an answer,' or simply 'I don't know.' People may have been surprised, some even shocked, but they seemed to understand. Perhaps I seemed human and frail like them.

There seems little place for such silence in the world of science, just as there is no way we can measure the therapeutic benefit of a friendly touch, but only a fool would deny that benefit there can be. I suspect that benefit will never be measured because it is not measurable and no scientific paper on it will ever be published in our learned journals. Our students will continue to be taught more about the chemistry of the body than about the alchemy of relationships. They will qualify, as we all have done, secretly believing that someone, somewhere, somehow, has the answers if we but know where to turn. They will, unconsciously, pass on that philosophy to their patients so that with each decade we shall see their 'Quick Fix' expectations growing and growing.

How often have I heard doctors mutter that their patients treat them no differently from repair men, often adding 'except that the plumber/electrician/washing machine engineer or whatever gets more per hour than I do.' I wonder if we doctors have only ourselves to blame. We so often portray ourselves as repair men, skilled at finding the fault and repairing it; much less skilled at explaining that something cannot be repaired or replaced and has come to the end of its life. Is it any wonder than people have unrealistic expectations of us and find it so easy to criticise and condemn when we disappoint them?

Why was working with the dying so rewarding, without question the greatest experience of my life? For many of the reasons we have just touched on – being with people on the loneliest journey of their lives, being their friend as well as their doctor, still being accepted and valued even when, in modern medical terms, we had so little to offer once their suffering was eased and their fear ventilated. As my old friend would have said – finding that that platform ticket was the most essential thing I would need.

But that same platform ticket was itself a pointer to greater truths which made this work, this ministry, so rich. What a mystery, what a paradox that a doctor has to come to the end of his life's work before he finds that mortally ill people know what ails them and what is to come long before they are 'told'; that people are much, much less frightened by the truth than by the unknown; that there comes a time when even modern medicine has no more to offer (difficult as it seems to be to believe that today), but the doctor is never as helpless as he or she feels. He still has himself or herself, with a touch of humour, a lifetime of experiences on which to draw, and the thing neither he nor anyone else will ever be able to measure, that deep innate love for his fellow human beings which first attracted him to this profession.

'I know you're a clever man, doctor, with lots of letters after your name but what I need now is your friendship, your humanity. Please be my friend now as well as my doctor.'

Life has so many 'ages' through which we pass, The Age of Schooling, the Age of Discovery, the Age of Parenting and now, for the author, the Age of Anecdotes, a term he prefers to Antiquity! Hours could be spent listening again to those throw away lines from patients of the last twenty odd years in the hospice. If only they had been said earlier. Would I have heard them, I wonder. Would I have been any better as a doctor and as a person?

'Don't ask me about my pain. Ask me about me, the man with the pain.'

'Oh the questions I've wanted to ask but no-one thought I knew what was happening.'

'I'm asking all these questions because I really want to know and I *need* to know.'

'I'm scared of the unknown. You see, doctor, I've never done this before.'

'Why did I only discover my true self when I was about to die and it was too late?'

'I'm really not scared of death but I'm terrified of what might happen *before* then.'

'It's so refreshing to meet a doctor who says he doesn't know. You're human!'

'These last few weeks have been the happiest time in my life.'

'Just sit beside me. You don't need to talk if you don't want to. Just be you.'

'Doctor, can I ask you – are *you* scared of dying?'

'Don't tell me lies. At this time of life I simply must know you're being honest.'

'I've given up asking for miracles – but perhaps hoping for dignity is asking a lot.'

'I'll never waste your time: I've just found how short and precious my own is!'

'When you feel wanted you feel you can do anything, even die well!'

'Yes I want a bit longer – to go round and apologize to everyone I've hurt!'

I regard it as tragic that we ever needed a so-called ' Hospice Movement' but it cannot be denied that it was needed. Swept along on the euphoric wave of medical progress we had become experts in diagnosis and sophisticated care for which we, and the world, should be eternally grateful. Let no one deny the advances of recent years but, at the same time, let no-one deny that our focus shifted from caring to curing. Doctors devoted their energies to cures, if such were possible, and patients came to expect them. When the spotlight focused on curing it was no longer on that less dramatic, less 'exciting' part of the spectrum, those who suffered usually in silence and could not be cured, the disadvantaged dying. One is reminded here of one of the pioneers in this work who observed 'The dead don't vote.' Before the Hospice Movement, before the evolution of specialist palliative care, the dying were in danger of being not only disadvantaged but neglected or forgotten.

All has changed. Around the world people are asking for palliative care and doctors are training to provide it and doing so eminently well. The scientific component of their work is exemplary. What remains is for us to listen to some of the things our patients and their loved ones are saying. They are further down the road of life than us. They deserve our attention and we need to hear because much of what they are teaching us could equip us for living as well as for our dying.

'What do we need?' I hear people ask.

'You'll need a platform ticket so that you can stand beside me. I'm not frightened, you know, but this is a very lonely experience which I haven't had before. You don't need to say anything. I just want you near me.'

Wouldn't this world be a better place if we all carried platform tickets.

Chapter 9

Tying up the Loose Ends

'It hath often been said that it is not death but dying which is terrible.'   Henry Fielding

Every now and then in any hospice or palliative care unit something happens which is so moving, so poignant, that words seem inadequate to describe it. Each time it happens those of us privileged to be working there feel deeply humbled yet glad to have been able to see it and experience it. Each in our own way, we come away changed, challenged, hopefully a little bit better to know and to live with. I cannot believe that anyone could witness some of the things I shall try to describe without being deeply affected. Let me describe a patient who only really came to know and appreciate his wife in his final days.

Old and young, people of all ages come in and go out of hospices. Tom was an ex-soldier who, as he would say 'had seen life'. He was a fund of stories, all interesting but some blood curdling and not designed for bedtime listening. He liked to be thought of as tough, macho, a man's man. 'I'm not frightened of death – seen too much of it in my time. Comes to us all, I always say.' He spoke convincingly, but who was he trying to convince?

One night I passed his room and saw the light on so went in for what he always spoke of as 'a crack', a joke or a chat. That night there was to be no joke. Tom was quietly crying into his pillow. I said nothing but sat on the bed.

'Have you seen my wife? Beautiful, isn't she? Always has been.

111

I've been a lucky man.'

I had indeed met his wife, one of the smallest ladies I have ever seen. Petite, pretty and so vivacious. Unbeknown to Tom she had talked to so many of us and spoken of her fears, not for herself and their son, but for Tom and how he would face death. She knew that under that tough, leathery exterior there was a softness few had seen. She had described him to me as her Malteser, hard on the outside but so soft inside.

Tom started to talk again. 'I've always had to do everything for her, you know. Typical woman, very pretty, but not able to make decisions or do things on her own. I always knew that without me she would be helpless, lost. You've heard me say I'm not afraid to die? Well that's true. It's not death that scares me, or did until tonight, but what it would do to that little woman. Without me she'd be lost, absolutely lost, I tell you. That's what I thought until tonight.'

He paused, looked away and I could see he was stifling a choke as tears began to show in his eyes. 'Do you know what happened tonight?' The question was rhetorical because, almost at once, he began to explain. 'She sat there where you are now and proceeded to tell me that she had made arrangements with the roof man to check our slates before the winter sets in, that she had been to a garage and asked what they would give her for my car because she needed the money more than the car, and finally she told me of her meeting with Peter's teacher at last night's Parent-Teacher Meeting at school. She is coping so well that I can't believe it. It's almost as if I've died already and she's showing me and showing the world that's she's got more about her than anyone has ever given her credit for, or certainly more than I have ever recognized.'

I asked him if what had really hurt was her behaving, as he put it, as if he had died already. No, not really, he said, though that had been uncomfortable. What had upset him was the discovery that they had spent so many years together and he had been blind to her gifts and her ability; he had been so preoccupied with himself and his macho image that he had never seen her for what she was, a truly remarkable lady.

'What's so upsetting is to realize that I never really knew her. I could have sworn that I knew everything that went on in her head and now I find I didn't. I get the feeling she knows me better than I know her.'

I tried to comfort him. 'You haven't done anything wrong, Tom, just not recognized what a wonderful person she really is, even better than you ever thought.' That was no comfort.

'I've wasted so much time putting on my macho act and pretending to be what I am not and, to make matters worse, not allowing her to be her real self. Doctor, try to keep me going for another few days if you can so that I can use these last days to show her how I love her. It's sort of the last thing I have to do in life.'

'How like men!' was all the nurses said when I recounted this story to them.

Sometimes the fault, if that is the right word, lies not with the one coming to the end of life but with those who love them. How they behave, how they show their love, makes such a difference to the dying person's final days.

Sheila and her husband had only been married for a few years and had no family. They were deeply in love, as they both kept telling us and as we kept reminding them was obvious to us all! Her eyes lit up when he came in and ever so gently put his arms round her and kissed her. At the end of each precious time together he would try to hold back his tears until she could no longer see him then the flood gates would open. He would come into the doctors' room or a little quiet room set aside for just such a need and cry uncontrollably as he recounted how happy they had been until cancer struck. Time after time he would ask 'How will I ever survive without her?'

The other person who loved her just as dearly was her mother.

Can any of us begin to imagine what it feels like to watch your young daughter die before you? Many of us remember the old lady, very much older than Sheila's mother, who visited the hospice to see her son and her daughter both dying at the same time. All she could say was 'It isn't fair. It isn't fair.' Sheila's mother must have thought the same but her pain was made worse by the fact that she had no time or respect for her son-in-law.

It sometimes seemed to us that they hated each other. Though we tried to arrange their visits for different times inevitably they often met, always standing on opposite sides of the bed scowling at each other. Sheila used to look from one to the other, helpless to intervene, her strength sapping away.

Try as we might, we could not reconcile the husband and mother-in-law. We pleaded, we remonstrated, we spoke to them separately and we spoke to them together, all to no avail. Always we focused on Sheila and the hell she was going through seeing them expressing such bitterness towards each other. I recall one day being so upset, and I suppose angry as well, that I spoke as I never normally do. 'For God's sake make your peace with each other and stop behaving like children.' To no avail.

Sheila lapsed into coma. On one side of the bed was mother, breaking her heart. On the other young husband, beside himself with grief and certain that there was no future for him now. Neither would speak to the other. I pleaded with them. I bullied them. 'For Sheila's sake, accept each other so that you can help each other and she can die in peace.'

Suddenly, and to our complete surprise, Sheila opened her eyes and spoke. 'Please accept each other. I can't die until you do.' With that she once again lapsed into coma, not responding to anything we doctors did to her. Try as we might, we could not rouse her. Even when she received an injection there was not a flicker of a response.

Twice more this happened. She seemed to come back from the dead, each time pleading with what little breath she had left that they accept each other and live in peace. None of us, doctors or nurses, had ever witnessed such a thing before. Here was a young woman all but dead, apparently able to control her dying so that she could see those nearest and dearest to her reconciled. Both of them seemed gripped not just by fear but by something greater. They stood motionless, gazing at the inert body just barely alive. Their eyes never left her until, at exactly the same time, without even looking up at each other, they both walked to the foot of the bed and took each other in their arms, and kissed and cried as I have rarely seen anyone do. He apologized to her that he had been so self-centred, lost in his grief and she said the same to him. Still locked in each other's arms they took their eyes off Sheila and looked at each other. Exactly at that moment there was a faint voice from the bed.

'Thank you both. Oh how I love you. Now I can go,' and with that, she died.

There are some things which we cannot explain. That was certainly one. However, though we cannot explain we can begin to understand. Here was yet another person who had a sense of mission in her all-too brief life, that of bringing together her adoring husband and her equally adoring mother, neither of whom could bear to lose her or to share her with anyone else. How seldom do we ask what our mission is in life. Do we doctors make any space in our hectic days for this dimension?

In the earliest days of the hospice we admitted a somewhat cantankerous old man who seemed to have not a single friend or relative. We soon found why. When you saw how bad-tempered he could be, and how rude to the nurses whenever they tried to help him, it was no wonder he was friendless. However, most of the nurses were infinitely more understanding and patient than I was and they persisted with their gentle, tolerant approach. His manner changed, the occasional kind word of appreciation was heard, and he became almost pleasant to care for. Only then did he mention a daughter. He had no idea what her address was, nor her telephone number. It took days for him to recall where he had last heard she was living and as many days again before the police in that town had tracked her down.

I phoned her. Very, very cautiously and, it must be said, reluctantly she admitted that she was his daughter. She had not seen him for many years and did not wish to see him now or ever again. My pleadings fell on deaf ears. When told he was dying she retorted that that was the best thing that had happened to him. I was politely but firmly asked never to make contact with her again. None of us knew what had caused this terrible rift, nor expected to find out. All she said was that after what he had done to her as a young girl she never wanted to see him again. She was happily married with two children and wanted nothing to destroy that happiness. Broken families sometimes seem to be the norm when you see the world through the eyes of a doctor!

He grew weaker as each day passed. Soon he was unable to get up without assistance and finally needed help even to sit up in bed for the tiny meals he agreed to take though he had no appetite. Not a day passed without him saying how he wanted to see that daughter but now he added, 'to ask her forgiveness before I go. You see, I've not been the best of fathers'.

One morning the nurses found him unconscious. The colour had drained from his face, his hands were cold and lifeless and his breathing was of the intermittent type we know is a sign that someone will die within a few hours. I think we all felt unbearably sad both for him and for that daughter but it was too late to do anything except phone her and report that he would die very, very soon. One of the nursing sisters did that, reassuring her that someone would be with him and that he seemed very peaceful at last. Just as she was about to put the phone down the daughter suddenly said 'I'll come up to see him straight away. I'm over 100 miles away so it may take two hours but I'll come nevertheless.' Sister urged her to drive carefully, recognizing that she was probably more upset than she liked to acknowledge.

She was met at the door and taken in his room. He was scarcely alive and to her, seeing him for the first time in years, it must have been a terribly distressing sight as she looked at the inert figure lying there. Tears began to well up in her eyes as she looked at the man she had thought she hated. If I had not been there myself I would never have believed what happened next. She bent down and kissed his forehead. 'It's me, Dad,' she said.

Immediately his eyes opened as if he had been having 'forty winks' after a good lunch. 'Oh, darling. It's good to see you. What time is it? Have you had any breakfast?'

'No, Dad, I haven't but that doesn't matter. There are things I want to say to you.'

'Well, come to think of it, there are things I want to say to you but they are better said after a good breakfast. Sister could you have someone bring us both a cooked breakfast please.' With that, he wriggled up in bed to make room for her to sit on it beside him and they sat there holding hands like a couple of love birds. The rest of us tiptoed out but could hear the occasional laugh and a lot of crying. A few minutes later in walked two of the domestic staff carrying trays of porridge, bacon and egg, toast and marmalade. They ate the lot! That itself was almost a miracle because he had not eaten for days.

By mid afternoon, when they had both enjoyed their lunch, they had called several of us in to hear that she had forgiven him, that he was delighted with the photographs of the grandchildren he had never seen, and that she felt she had done the right thing travelling all that way to see him. However, there were those hundred miles to travel back before it was dark 'because John and the boys will be wanting their tea.'

'Dad, I must go. God bless.' She could say no more but her tears said everything.

'I'll see you to the door, little one.' The man who had needed assistance with everything for so many days, who could neither eat nor move in his bed, now threw back his bed clothes, and took her arm as they slowly walked to the door of his room. It seemed the most normal, natural thing to do.

They hugged each other for the last time. 'I love you, Dad.' Her tears said the rest.

'Thank you for forgiving me,' he whispered as she let go of him. For a moment he just stood there, one hand on the door, watching her disappear. Then he turned and saw me standing there.

'Wasn't that just wonderful? Time to go, doctor. Thank you all for everything.'

We helped him back into bed. Five minutes later he died.

Finished business, as people call it. We are all familiar with the feeling that we have work to do or jobs to complete, trivial as they may be in our ordinary, humdrum lives. Often we know what the tasks are and if they are unpleasant or difficult we find ourselves putting them off so that sometimes they never get done. At other times we cannot identify the unfinished business, just having a curious sense, almost impossible to describe, of something which leaves us disturbed. Very commonly it is an interpersonal thing, something we have to say to someone, a person we should apologize to, an unpleasant decision to make sooner rather than later. Wherever we are, whatever the time of day, we have a sense of something we should do and not put off any longer.

Time after time people in the hospice would talk to us about this feeling and how they, as the rest of us do so regularly, had put off doing anything about it until it was too late. Perhaps they became too frail or the person they wanted to speak to never appeared. The longed for and so often postponed opportunity was lost for ever. The unfinished business was seldom anything as mundane as writing a will or inserting a codicil, answering a letter or completing a book, important as they might seem. More usually it was a wish to apologize or to explain, or a search for reassurance about something said or done many years before.

There must be few things sadder than seeing a person die, unable to make their peace with someone because they are both too stubborn or the other party never visits. Even worse is the longed for reconciliation which never happens because one party cannot forgive and forget. So many of our arguments and disagreements seem so paltry when life is short. Would any of us behave differently if we knew how often a hospice patient remarks 'How I wish I had done something about this earlier, and now it's too late?'

Chapter X

The Easy Way Out?

'A time to kill and a time to heal'.

We have already spoken at length about hospice care and 'quality of life'. Hospice care is also maintaining dignity though some might say dignity and quality of life are almost the same thing. Certainly one leads on to the other. It is amazing how some people can remain so dignified yet have what appears to the onlooker as an appalling quality of life.

Noble sentiments but what do they mean? Quality of life we have looked at briefly, but what do we mean by dignity?

It used to be said that hospice care was developed to relieve pain and suffering. That was true though what was meant by suffering was usually physical or emotional, the myriad fears and secret feelings of those coming to the end of life. Some saw and promoted euthanasia as a dignified alternative to the hospice approach. Why suffer pain when all suffering can be ended by euthanasia, went the argument. More recently, as we have made progress in controlling physical problems we have come to appreciate that every bit as distressing to a dying person is this sense of being a burden. Today we can have terminally ill people completely free of pain, physically comfortable in every respect, their ever fear addressed, their family lovingly and skilfully supported yet still they long to die – *because they feel they are a burden on family or society.*

Never a day passes without some politician telling us what it costs to keep a patient in hospital, what better care could be given if there was money to fund it. We are told, often subliminally, how expensive it is to look after the increasing number of retired and elderly in our society and what a problem this is going to become in a few years time. Those same people are watching their televisions like the rest of us. Not only can they no longer work but some of them know how expensive their hospital treatment has been, know that it cannot keep them alive indefinitely and they begin to wonder if the last and most noble thing they can do for their country and those they love is to die at a time and in a manner of their own choosing – euthanasia or physician-assisted suicide.

The mention of that brings back such memories to me because, contrary to what people might expect, euthanasia is often talked about, *though never performed,* in hospices. Occasionally a patient will speak of it, as I shall tell you, but frequently it is the relatives who raise the issue.

One of the greatest honours for a doctor is to be asked to look after a medical colleague coming to the end of his life. That happened many times in the hospice where I worked. An honour always, but very often a challenging experience. You see in the other man or woman someone who has had many of the same experiences you have had yourself, many of the thrills, many of the disappointments and sadnesses. Into your hands has come someone who also has cared for the dying, felt the helplessness you have known, and shed tears of frustration or anger. They have now reached the end of life and, like everyone else, deserve nothing but the best; the best relief of suffering, the best listening to the opened hearts, the best comfort for their loved ones. They come into your care to be looked after but give far more than they receive.

One such was a retired general practitioner who had already suffered from his terminal illness for more than three years when he was admitted to see if we could ease his unremitting pain. I have to admit it was not easy and both the doctor and I were probably equally surprised and delighted when we succeeded. Free of pain he became a fund of stories of practice in 'the old days', the days of kitchen surgery, of working every day of the year without a break of any kind, of babies born at home, sitting up all night with the dying and feeling helpless in the face of other illnesses for which there was no cure and little effective palliation. We became good friends, able to laugh with and at each other.

Hardly a day passed without him telling me in one way or another how strongly he supported legalizing (or decriminalizing, as some would say) voluntary euthanasia. His argument was always the same. Why leave a person to live out a useless life, useless to him, to his family and to society which needed the precious resources being wasted on him. Life was only worth living if it was useful. If usefulness had ceased and the person was keen to be on their way, then perform euthanasia. 'Look at me' he kept saying, 'eager to die, long past my "shelf life" or "sell by" date, not frightened to die but horrified by the strain all this is on my wife. I cannot begin to tell you how keen I am for you to end my life and, admit it, no one would ever know!'

One morning I told him that I would be busy the rest of the day teaching medical students visiting the hospice. He pushed himself up in bed and looked me straight in the eye. 'I'll bet you'd never let me speak to them for half an hour, would you? I could spend that time telling them that we have a right to die, a right to end our life (or have someone do it for us) when and how we choose, and that refusing me that right is a denial of my autonomy. Ha, what have you to say to that?'

'You're on,' I replied 'but not one minute longer than half an hour. You're more tired than you like to admit!' He was thrilled and immediately began to make a few notes in readiness. For my part, I wondered if this was the height of my irresponsibility. When I told my nurse and medical colleagues I was greeted with shaking heads which spoke louder than words.

I took a group of about twelve or fifteen final year students into his room and introduced them to him. I am sure they realized that this was quite an honour to be taught not only by someone able to give them insights into what it feels to be near the end of life, but for that teacher to be one of their own profession. I certainly had never had such a tutorial in my far-off student days. Even before I had closed the door behind me I heard him say 'Ladies and gentlemen, I propose to spend the next thirty minutes telling you how strongly I believe euthanasia should be possible for people like me.' I almost envied those students having such a teacher. I began to wonder what other teachers in the Medical School would have to say when they heard what was being taught in tutorials at the hospice.

Thirty minutes later I knocked on his door and went in. It looked as though no-one had moved since I left him. Their eyes were fixed on him, fascinated, moved probably in a way they had never experienced in their training. He brought his talk to a dramatic end.

'There you have it, ladies and gentlemen, a passionate plea from the heart of a man who has spent a lifetime caring for the sick and dying and is now, in effect, in his own condemned cell; a man of no use to man or beast, a man who feels and knows he is a burden on society, a man who is ready to die, nay keen to die and this good doctor here, for I know him to be a good doctor, will not help me, is not allowed to help me, because of the law of the land.'

On any other occasion there ought to have been a burst of applause. All eyes turned to me. The doctor did the same, smiled as if to thank me for giving him such a platform, then looked down at the sheath of notes and laboratory reports I was carrying.

'Are those my latest blood results you've got there?'

'Yes, they've just arrived. I'll come back later when the students have gone and go over them with you, shall I?'

'You'll do no such thing! I want to know them now. What's my haemoglobin?'

'Not good, I'm afraid. It's fallen to 8G.'

'My God! Don't just stand there. At that level I need a blood transfusion as soon as possible or I'll die.'

How can I possibly describe what happened next? Every student sat transfixed, only their eyes moving between me and the patient. No-one said a word. Indeed, what word was there to say! The patient had been sitting on the edge of his bed but now he stood up, his hands clasping his head as he muttered time after time 'Oh my God, what a fool! Oh what a fool!

'Derek, may I have just one more minute with these young people please? Please stay and hear what I have to say to them. I owe it to them all and to you in particular.

'I want to take back every single word I said to you. I had not realized until today that we can be useful, as I hope I have been to you, without realizing it, without doing anything extraordinary. Neither had I realized how precious is life even to an old fool like me. I hope you will forgive me.' With that he flopped down on the bed, his head buried in his hands.

One student stepped forward from the group and took the doctor's hand in his in a gesture which seemed totally appropriate but which I suspect he had never done before.

'Thank you, sir. Thank you for the best tutorial we have ever had. Thank you for just being you, sir!' With that they all left his room and left us together as we needed to be.

We all know there are certain people and certain events which stay in your memory when most others fade away. One patient, and indeed his lovely wife and daughters, will remain with me for ever. He, like the doctor I have spoken of, was a highly educated and very articulate man. No-one in the world deserves to suffer but this man seemed to suffer more troubles than almost anyone I have met in my medical career. His cancer had 'eaten away' the lower part of his abdomen, blocked the drainage from his legs so that they had swelled up to resemble tree trunks, and created such an appalling, all pervasive smell around him that we all felt nauseated and ill just being near him, in spite of all that modern medicine could offer. Tragically, the upper half of his body was unaffected for, if it had been, his survival would have been shortened. His brain was as active and sharp as when he had taken his post-graduate doctorate many years before.

He too asked to be allowed to speak to professional visitors, this time a group of thirty or so general practitioners spending a week with us. They were all very experienced doctors. I wheeled him into the room, sat down beside him, and introduced him to the group, telling them that in the next thirty minutes he would try to describe what it is like to have that illness and know that death is the only outcome.

'Doctors, I should like to start by telling you that Derek here – I trust I may use your first name – is one of the best doctors I have ever had the pleasure to meet.'

I was embarrassed. This was not what he was supposed to say. 'Hold on! No commercials please!'

Pretending to look very stern he turned and said to me 'I haven't finished yet! I was about to tell them that I would have *liked* to say that but I can't. You're an awful doctor!' His eyes twinkled, a few titters were heard coming from the audience, and I resigned myself to hearing out the rest of what promised to be an upsetting half hour.

'He's the best doctor I have ever met when it comes to pain. I came in here begging to die or to be bumped off if you want to know, unable to stand any more pain, and look at me today – absolutely free from pain, and all thanks to him. Derek, thank you! But I am more than pain – I am a man who hates the sight of his own body, a man who cannot even shower without help, a man who cannot even go to the toilet without help, a man who cannot stand without help, a man who stinks, a man who is utterly, totally useless. Do you all hear me – useless! What have you done for that, Derek?' He almost spat the words out.

He then went on to describe how lacking in dignity he felt, how painful it was to be so dependent, how embarrassing it was to have to have his loving wife do the most intimate things for him. At one point he broke down when he asked if anyone could imagine what it was like, after a wonderfully happy marriage, to have to sleep in another room because of the odour filling his bed; what it was like to want to hug your wife of so many years and be unable to do it because it so upset them both.

Suddenly he fell silent. I did nothing because it felt appropriate. Everyone in the room was profoundly moved and, a sight I had never seen before, quite a few of the doctors were wiping away tears. I turned and looked at him, expecting to see him crying again but he was sitting very serene, very composed.

'Ladies and gentlemen, I came in here today planning to tell you how passionately I want euthanasia. I meant it. I was determined to win you over. However, I have seen some of you crying just as I have cried. I have realized that euthanasia is not the answer for me or indeed for anyone. I would never dream of asking Derek to perform it and now I realize I would never ask any of you. I came in here today wanting you to know how desolate you feel when you are useless . . . but seeing you all listening to me I see that I am not useless. I have only just discovered this afternoon that a wreck like me is still needed. Thank you for listening.

'Derek, give my wheelchair a kick-start please . . . you're good at that!' and once again those eyes twinkled as he winked at me for all to see.

It would be naive to imagine that two such stories answered all the well-rehearsed arguments of voluntary euthanasia enthusiasts. They merely illustrate an oft-overlooked fact. When 'the time comes' we often feel differently and react differently about things than we did when we were in robust health. There are few statements more foolish than 'I know exactly what I shall want/do when the time comes.'

What we must never forget, particularly if we are in the 'caring professions' is that a request for euthanasia is actually a plea for better care. I suspect that most people are not keen to die any earlier than they need to. What they want – indeed what they have every right to expect – is comfort, dignity, dying without agony, being told nothing but truth and hearing no more lies. The very word euthanasia should be like a starter's gun, sending us off as fast as possible to correct a wholly unacceptable situation.

Let's return to that other point though. How different are reality and theory. Do we not all go through life confidently saying what we will do or say when something happens. Politicians do it all the time! They promise that when they get into power they will change this, alter something else and bring in yet another improvement. Soon when they find it all much more difficult than they had ever imagined, they begin to make excuses. They blame those who were in power before them. Seldom do they admit that part of the problem is that they themselves now see things differently. Wasn't it Sir Peter Ustinov who said he could not bear to be a politician, right all the time? Why are most of us so confident and self-opinionated as to presume to know precisely how we shall react when such-and-such happens to us? Hospice care is full of examples of opinion changing, just as it is full of examples of people changing!

'You won't get me accepting chemotherapy, I can tell you! I've seen too much of what it does to you. When my time comes and some oncologist suggests I get chemotherapy I shall refuse. I shall get all the family together, settle my affairs while I am still able and clear of mind, say good-bye to them all and then let nature take its course. I'm damned if I'm going to be made sick and bald and miserable for the sake of an extra month or two!' The voice of a doctor.

Oh, how often have I heard this said. In fact when that sad day comes he is there, like the rest of us, accepting anything which might give another year or two, or even as little as a few months. His change of mind has little to do with the fact that chemotherapy is today much less upsetting than it used to be; that only a handful of people lose their hair because of a particular drug they are taking. It is far more a reflection of human behaviour. When 'the time comes', whatever that means, we often surprise ourselves by what we do and how we cope. That is one of the countless things which makes hospice care so fascinating.

One of the first people we were invited to see in his own home was a strong, one might almost describe him as vehement, advocate of euthanasia. It seems like yesterday that he asked me to sit and listen to him because, as he put it 'there may not be a better time to explain to you why people like me need and deserve euthanasia. When people like me get to this stage that I'm at we have every right to be given something to let us go.' Doctors are taught to give the impression of having all the time in the world to listen to those in need, even when, in fact, they are working against the clock. I was already far behind time but could not say that to him. I sat down and was treated to about half an hour's lecture, or to be honest, harangue. I sat beside him, silent but very conscious that he was having twinges of pain. It was past the time for his regular dose of morphine. Suddenly he stopped lecturing me and turned to his daughter, a qualified nurse.

'Time for my medicine dear.' She began to measure it out, with infinite care as she must have done for hundreds of people in the past. 'Careful, careful, for goodness sake. If I get too much of that it'll kill me. For God's sake be careful, dear.' She looked at me, smiled and shook her head.

Sometimes a change of mind can be embarrassing, particularly if past opinions have been strongly held and publicly expressed. I suspect few of us would have the courage and the decency to do what I am now to describe. We would find it difficult to admit we were wrong, or that even the most strongly-held views can change. It must be even more difficult when doing so means the loss of friends and their respect and understanding.

When his GP phoned the hospice to ask either my consultant colleague or me to visit this gentleman, rather than passing on all the details in the routine way to one of our specially trained PAs, instead he asked to speak to me because of the sensitive nature of the case. He asked if the name Jock Brown meant anything to me (and here, as always, the name is changed to respect confidentiality). It certainly did, for this man was an office bearer in a branch of the Voluntary Euthanasia Society. There could be no stronger advocate of active euthanasia nor a more vocal and articulate one, though to give him his due, his sincerity and his integrity were beyond question. 'He is on his last legs and wonders if after all he has said about the hospice and your work, you would agree to see him? Believe me, he's suffering appallingly and I feel helpless. The trouble is he feels so embarrassed and so full of remorse. He seems to think you'll leave him to suffer because of what he's said. Needless to say I've done my best to explain that that would never happen. When can you visit him?'

That same afternoon I found myself on his doorstep, quite apprehensive, I must admit. The door opened and there was this frail, unshaven, unkempt little man standing there. We laughed together because at exactly the same time, as if we had been programmed to do so, we both reached out both hands. Instead of shaking hands in the usual way we both seemed to feel it more appropriate to hug each other though we had never met face to face. Somehow it felt right though how one ever knows what is appropriate always puzzles me.

'Can you forgive me?' he asked when we had gone into his little bedroom.

'I haven't the faintest idea what you're talking about so let's get on with what really matters! Tell me all about how you're feeling and how I can help you.' The past slipped behind us and a bond of friendship was quickly made. Within hours he was admitted to the hospice, within a day or so he was free from pain and eating again, and then he had to face up to the dramatic U-turn he had made and what his friends would say. I suspected that they would try to persuade him to go home or would castigate him for breaking ranks, but no. Most seemed secretly to admire him even if they could scarcely understand why he had changed. Others saw the humour in what was happening, as he did. You see at that time the method of suicide advocated by his erstwhile friends and camp-followers was to take about 50 tablets of paracetamol, washed down with a half bottle of whisky, then to pull a plastic bag over one's head and sleep away.

'Doctor, how's the hospice's stock of whisky?' he asked, knowing that each night it was offered to any who enjoyed a traditional Scots nightcap, or indeed any sassenach who took it for 'medicinal purposes'. 'I'll just keep accepting all they bring in to me and soon you'll have all the paracetamol and whisky the hospice needs for the next few months!'

Perhaps his last words were the most telling of his life. Aware that the end was near, but obviously very comfortable, he took my hand, as a nurse held the other one, and said 'Is this all there is to it?' I nodded. Scarcely a moment later he died.

Why he had changed his mind we shall never know. Why should we risk embarrassing him? Perhaps we were both right. He had advocated euthanasia because too many people suffer unnecessarily and he saw this speedy way out as an answer to such suffering. We saw hospice care as one response to the suffering. We were each committed to serving the same people but in vastly different ways. What is so interesting, however, is how people change the views they have held and fought for over many years.

It must not be assumed that whenever a hospice programme is started there is widespread rejoicing in the local medical community. Far, far from it. The initial reaction is usually one of surprise that anyone should ever have thought it necessary. This is usually followed by slight irritation, to say the least, at the inference that care for the terminally ill is less than adequate and could be improved ('none of my patients has ever come back and complained to me') followed by a long period in which local doctors refer the occasional patient and carefully monitor how they are cared for. The turning point for many is when a member of their own family needs the best possible care. The GP or consultant who has never hesitated to express grave reservations about hospice and palliative care now has no qualms about calling in a consultant in palliative medicine to see mother, or asking for her to be admitted. It must also be added that these same colleagues are usually generous in the extreme in their appreciative comments about the care, and then go on to refer patients as a routine.

Chapter XI

Families and Friends

'A time to embrace and a time to refrain from embracing'.

It is generally acknowledged that the so-called Hospice Movement has brought about several welcome, and some would say long overdue, improvements in the care of the terminally ill. These are not merely impressions or sentimental anecdotes. Research has confirmed it. There is, for example, evidence that the relief of pain and other distressing symptoms has so improved in many hospitals that it equals that to be found in most hospices. That must be good news.

What is not so widely known is that people do not necessarily have to go into a hospice or palliative care unit to receive excellent care at that time of their lives. All across the country they can get it in the wards of ordinary hospitals where there are 'hospital palliative care teams' composed of consultants in palliative medicine, nurse specialists and, backing them up, social workers, therapists and chaplains (or pastoral care workers as they call them in North America). Even when there is not a ward designated for hospice-type care these teams move around the hospital, seeing patients in medical and surgical wards, in oncology, in fact anywhere where their professional colleagues feel they might be able to contribute to better care, not only for the patient but also for the relatives and close friends. A physical, bricks and mortar hospice can offer a very special atmosphere, as this book sets out to illustrate, but it is not essential for dignified, compassionate care of those with a short time to live.

It has also to be borne in mind that the principles of palliative care are not, nor ever have been, the monopoly of hospices and their dedicated staff. They are in fact the principles of all good care, whether given by nurses or doctors, whether they are GPs or hospital specialists, whether the patient has a relatively minor illness or a life-threatening one. The lessons we learn from caring for the dying apply equally well to the care of people in illness and suffering whatever the cause, wherever they are. In health circles it is now acknowledged that everyone has the right to receive palliative care and that is the professional and moral responsibility of every doctor and nurse to provide it. What has been so unique in Britain in the past 10-15 years has been the growth and development of *specialist* palliative care, a development now replicated in Australia, New Zealand and Hong Kong but nowhere else in the world. The word specialist is well chosen. It does not describe whether or not the doctor or nurse works full or part time in the field but whether they have undergone advanced training and gained many years of experience exclusively in that area of work. It might be of interest to readers to know that in Britain a medical specialist in palliative medicine, a consultant in palliative medicine, must always have a higher medical qualification (usually a Membership of one of the medical Royal Colleges), have completed his or her training in another specialty such as oncology, chest medicine, or general practice, *then* undergone a further four years training in palliative care to ensure that he possesses a high degree of expertise in the rare as well as the common manifestations and challenges of the specialty. Similarly palliative care nurse practitioners/specialists have taken advanced courses, gained additional qualifications, and worked for many years in palliative care before being granted specialist status.

I explain all this, not by way of boasting, but to demonstrate that there is much expertise in both the small hospices and the famous specialist palliative care units of our land, and flowing from them, into most of the large hospitals of the country, so that people need not always move into a hospice to get good care.

There is now good evidence that the relief of suffering can be as skilled and effective in the large hospital as in the little hospice, though many people still say they prefer the smaller homely unit than the 'impersonal' hospital, forgetting that it is there that further investigations can be done, if needs be, and it is usually there where they have been known for years and come to know and trust the staff.

There is, however, one aspect of palliative care which appears to be better provided in a special hospice unit than in the larger hospital; that is the care and support of the relatives and immediate friends, an integral part of all good care but one easily overlooked in the rush and bustle which characterizes hospital care. This may be one reason why hospices get high popularity ratings when surviving relatives are interviewed. If they were made to feel welcome, they assume the patient also was. If some of their apprehensions were addressed, then hopefully the same applies to the one they lost. Certainly hospice care teaches us all many things we might otherwise never have known about relatives and friends.

Some of the stories recounted in this book have mentioned how long some couples had been married, presumably giving them a unique and sympathetic understanding of each other, but it seems this is not always so. We have seen how people desperately try to keep painful information from each other, usually to no avail, in my experience. The number of times I have met someone who had been successfully shielded from that truth can be counted on the fingers of one hand. Loving couples also claim that they know exactly how the other is feeling and what they are suffering, albeit in silence. Once again this is being shown not to be true, sad to say. It seems from good research that even the most sensitive spouse or partner always overestimates the pain and the anxiety of the loved one with the terminal illness. What they perceive as his or her pain is actually the reflection of *their* pain and anguish. So keen are they that he suffers as little as possible that they keep reporting pain when they could equally usefully be telling the nurses and doctors how *they* feel.

A return of appetite is always a good thing to see, and indeed to experience if you are the patient who had lost it, so this story will be familiar to many of us who have ever lost their appetite. I passed the bed of a gentleman who had come in with no appetite whatsoever, much to the sadness and frustration of his wife who had tried everything she knew to tempt him. There he was, a few days after coming in, with his lunchtray in front of him, on it a small bowl of soup, a plate of lamb, new potatoes, peas and mint sauce, and beside that a little dish of trifle. He had enjoyed a sherry before he started lunch and on the bedside locker was a miniature Scotch malt whisky for 'afters'. He looked up from admiring his tray to joke with me 'No doctor, I don't care how much you plead – you are not getting that miniature!' I pretended to be disappointed and went on my way sulking.

Not five minutes later his wife, who had just come in to see him, stopped me in the corridor. She was flushed with anger. 'How dare you leave my husband in such agony. This is supposed to be a place where you can take away their pain, not leave them suffering like that.'

Clearly something dramatic had happened in those few minutes since I had been with him. I quickly got her into a nearby room whilst I rushed back to him, calling a nurse to come with me. As we both went in to him he laughed and shook his head 'No, doctor, it won't make any difference even if you bring a nurse with you to beat me up – you're simply not getting my whisky and that's that!'

The poor man suddenly noticed that we were both very serious. He realized, or at least he suspected, what had happened. 'Has that wife of mine been at you? I've tried to tell her I haven't a pain in my body but she tells me I have so when I kept denying it she thought I was just being brave and said she would get you. I'm terribly sorry, both of you, but how do you persuade someone you're comfortable when they don't want to believe you.'

All we needed to do was to let his wife see him as he really was, and explain that someone in dreadful pain does not finish a glass of sherry, a three-course lunch, then a small whisky and manage to laugh as much as he was doing! Eventually she was convinced and managed to laugh about it but many others have not been so easily reassured. What are we to make of this? It surely cannot be because they want their loved one to suffer or, as it were, will them to have pain. Equally it cannot be because they do not trust each other, though it might well be because they have little trust in, or respect for, the doctors and nurses they encounter. Our reputation for easing pain is appallingly bad, hence the origins of the Hospice movement.

One very likely reason may be that everyone assumes that cancer equals pain. 'You can't have cancer without pain' is the widely held belief. If people were to be stopped in the High Street, Anytown and asked what two words come into their minds when they hear the word Cancer there is no doubt whatsoever they would say death and pain. Combine that misunderstanding with the fact that pain is such a subjective experience, almost impossible to measure, and we have a good reason for relatives to adopt their protector-advocate role. 'You have cancer, therefore you have pain. No-one will notice you have pain and, knowing you as I do, you will not mention it yourself, so I shall do so on your behalf.'

Of course there may be other reasons for their concern and unintentional exaggeration of pain and anxiety, not least one of disappointment and even regret bordering on guilt that they were unable to continue to keep the patient at home. Their vigilance in spotting and reporting pain confirms for them that it was right he or she came into the hospice rather than remaining at home. Wives often seemed quite hurt when their husbands regained their appetite in the hospice, as if the loss of appetite had been their fault. The explanation was actually very simple. At home they could often smell the cooking, or were offered too much, or were cajoled into eating – all designed to reduce rather than increase appetite. In a hospice or hospital the cook does not break his heart when some food is returned untouched whereas at home the poor wife feels that she has failed him in his hour of need. If she cannot even tempt him with her traditionally excellent cooking, what *can* she now do for him?

Pick up any book on caring for the dying and it is certain to repeat the myth that, given the chance and the choice, all dying people want to remain at home and to die in their own beds. Not only do the patients want to stay at home but it is equally the ambition of the carers to make it possible. So says the myth, but myth it is, according to excellent research and indeed the experience of hundreds of hospice workers over the years. The fact is that most people do want to be cared for at home, for as long as possible, provided the care given by the professionals is good, provided they handle any emergency with skill and with speed, provided the family are supported and their needs recognized and met, and finally, provided a safety net is provided in the form of a hospice bed should it ever be needed. The frailer they get, the more skilled palliation they need, the more the loving relatives and friends have to do, the more ready the patients are to go into the hospice or even back to their original ward in the hospital. Just as the patient is coming round to accepting that, so also is the family beginning to feel the strain and the weariness, but often dare not say so lest they are seen as uncaring or more concerned about themselves than about their loved one.

It also has to be admitted that our society is less and less comfortable with people dying at home, in stark contrast to the days of our grandparents where it was the norm. It makes you wonder whether this is a passing phase before we return to the old pattern, just as we went through a few decades when it was regarded as an obscenity for a woman to have her baby at home but now we are returning to that practice. I have encountered several people who were clearly caring most excellently but who asked for their loved one to be admitted because so many neighbours, friends and even fellow church members kept expressing surprise that the doctor had not yet made arrangements to 'get him in'.

It was not uncommon to be met on the doorstep by an anxious wife or daughter when a family doctor had invited us to visit someone at home, but seldom have I sensed such apprehension and anxiety as when we arrived at one house where the lady of the house was actually standing there looking out for us and waving the nursing sister and myself to hurry in. It seems her husband had had a terrible night because of uncontrolled pain and sickness. Nobody had had a wink of sleep, as was obvious when we went in and saw the ravages of tiredness and grief etched on every face. 'Doctor, we can't take much more of it,' said a daughter, obviously speaking for everyone. 'For God's sake help him please.'

Two days later the family doctor phoned and asked if I would visit again. 'The change has been dramatic and it'll do you good to see it. In any case, the family are desperate to see you. Very many thanks for all your help.' Expecting that it would be a little speech of gratitude I prepared to accept their thanks with the surprise and humility for which I and most doctors are not famed.

The scene was indeed totally changed. His wife stood on the doorstep but was calm and serene. She looked years younger after two good nights sleep. Several of the family met me in the hall as I walked in and started to bound upstairs two at a time. 'Where are going, doctor? He's not upstairs today. He's down here waiting for you.' Everyone laughed as I spun round and came down to meet him and get the best bear hug he could manage. He signalled me to sit down in the middle of this wonderfully happy family circle.

The eldest daughter spoke for them all. 'When are you taking Daddy in?'

All eyes were on me, except John's. His were fixed on some

spot in the carpet, studiously avoiding mine. I expressed surprise that they were talking about him coming in when he was obviously so comfortable at last and they were all doing a wonderful job looking after him. I explained, in all honesty, that he would not get as good care in the hospice and, if they did decide to keep him at home he would have community nurses, MacMillan nurses and their family doctor all visiting and he might even be able to come to the Day Hospice. If ever things became so difficult that he needed many more hands to look after him he could come in then. 'What do you feel yourself?' I asked John.

At first he said nothing but the others scrambled to have their say. Apparently neighbours had been shocked that two days before I had not immediately offered a hospice bed. How, they asked, could I be so insensitive as to walk into a sickroom and see someone suffering as he was and not arrange for immediate admission where there were doctors and nurses well able to care for him. How cold, callous and uncaring doctors were becoming. Their minister had also expressed surprise that a family should be expected to be up at night, taking it in turns to help John, especially when the church had so recently given all the proceeds of a 'Bring and Buy Sale' to the hospice! Several people had met them in the street and said how surprised they too were that the family had not demanded admission. 'It's made us all feel we are not doing the right thing for Daddy.' I looked at John.

'I only want what is best for them all, doctor.'

That was the end of the matter. Next day he came in, still saying he was doing it willingly though primarily for them, not for himself, something that we heard hundreds and hundred of patients say over the years. The sad thing to my mind, is that those who do keep their loved one at home, assisted by the excellent family doctors, community and Macmillan nurses we have now, without exception find it a profoundly rewarding experience, sad and demanding as it certainly is. It is rare for anyone to say they regret doing it and we have good reason to think they also come through their bereavement better than those whose loved one died in hospital or hospice, difficult as this is to assess.

Of course, it has to be admitted that we are not always as sensitive to the strain on the relatives that we should be. We too easily forget that they have watched the patient in dramatic ups and downs or 'relapses and remissions' as doctors call them. They can be so ill, so weak that no-one expects them to recover but recover they do. Weeks or months may pass before they go downhill again, taking with them the hopes and the dreams of those who love them. Everything looks so bad that anyone prepares for the worst but, perhaps as a result of new treatment or an operation or a few doses of radiotherapy, health returns yet again and with it, hope and happiness. No wonder it has been called the Roller Coaster of Caring. Needless to say there has to come a time when health and strength do not return as they did in the past. It is met either with incredulity that there is really no further treatment, nothing to bring about a short term reprieve *or* immense relief that there will be no more ups and downs, but who would dare to admit that they felt a sense of relief being told that the end really was nigh for the person they love.

How often we have had people say when being told how critically ill someone was 'Oh, I've been told that more times than I can count, doctor. I know he'll make it.' How often? Well, about as often as we've had people whisper to us that they can't take any more, cannot face any more sleepless nights, cannot manage any more visiting when they do not know what to say or what to do.

Many people succumb to such societal pressures as we have described but they often feel they have to live up to societal expectations and norms in other ways. We have been brought up to think of grief as a time of crying, total helplessness and of hopelessness but this is far from true. Examples have been given in this book of people who possibly surprised others, and certainly themselves, by being so resourceful; taking on responsibilities and tasks previously always done by the loved one who is now so ill.

We must not overlook those who cannot grieve. Perhaps it would be more correct to say 'those who cannot grieve any more' for their problem is that the one they love may have been unconscious or confused for weeks or even months, or if not actually unable to respond to them, has been so totally different from their previous selves that they are like strangers. This was eloquently explained to me by a lady whose bank manager husband had a brain tumour, depriving him of speech, then of his acute intellect and finally even of his sparkling, witty, considerate nature. For weeks he lay inert and unresponsive, his eyes no longer sparkling as they used to, his every bodily function dependent on his wife. Eventually he came into the hospice but we were soon conscious that she was ill at ease, as if she was embarrassed.

'I've just realized I am suppose to cry and look sad, but I can't,' she said. 'You see I've gone through that stage long ago. In fact, I feel as though I buried Hamish more than a month ago so I haven't any tears left in me. I've dried up. That man you see in the bed over there is not really my Hamish, he's someone else as far as I'm concerned, so how am I expected to sit crying beside him? I just want to be at home with the kids, trying to make sense of our new life without him, not sitting here beside someone who doesn't know me, can't speak and is unconscious most of the time. I supposed you're all shocked but there we are. I can't help it. I can see he's in no pain and that he's getting good care so why shouldn't I be at home with the kids who've lost their daddy?'

Many years ago when the hospice was in its infancy and so many doctors and nurses wanted to see it I had the pleasure of taking round a clinical psychologist, a very gentle, sensitive person. When we returned to my office he said he had enjoyed seeing the place but he had a question for me. How did we select the patients? Before I could explain that there was actually no selection – they simply came in as they were referred by family doctors and consultants according to their many needs, he went on to say that we obviously selected people according to whether or not they were happily married because in all the rooms where I had taken him were people who were happily married! Did we ever accept others? I was taken aback and, at first, thought he was genuinely asking a question but, as the reader will realize, he was challenging me.

'What do you do to help someone whose love has long dried up, someone who almost hates the one who is dying, someone who sits by the bedside only out of a sense of duty? If you now tell me you don't do anything I shall ask why you are adding to their burden in life, for burden it most certainly is!' I asked him to advise us how to help such people.

'Just bear in mind we are not talking about a rarity but a commonplace. In Britain one third of marriages end in divorce as we all know. I think it's safe to assume that another third are not all enjoying marital bliss but are putting on a good show for the sake of the children, their jobs and their neighbours, leaving perhaps a third who are as happy as you and I are with our partners. When you are talking to people here don't beat about the bush. Be direct and ask the nearest relatives exactly how they are feeling, giving them a chance to talk about something they've probably never dared say to anyone else. Believe me, the benefit could be quite dramatic.'

Not half an hour after he left I saw a lady sitting by the bedside of her husband, newly admitted to our care. They were not talking, but that, of course, could have been because they were feeling ill at ease or, like many happily married couples, able to sit and enjoy each other's company without necessarily talking all the time. I spoke to her and invited her to drop in to see me on her way home so that we could get to know each other.

After the usual formalities and polite conversation I asked her what she was feeling 'deep inside' and to my surprise she suddenly exploded with 'you won't keep him going will you and expect me to sit beside him every day? I'm not such a hypocrite and I'm a lousy actress.'

Then the full story came tumbling out. They had drifted further and further apart until finally both agreed that divorce was the best course to take. An appointment was made for them to see their lawyer one afternoon after he had visited his doctor for the results of a routine chest x-ray. That x-ray had revealed lung cancer. The appointment with the lawyer was cancelled and she determined to stay with him, helping in every way possible but little realizing that his life expectancy might be measured in years not months. Two years had passed during which she had had to do more and more for him, seeing him through radiotherapy, several hospital admissions and now finally his admission to the hospice. She had had to give up her job to look after him and felt increasingly angry with him for having his cancer. 'I know it isn't his fault and that it's ridiculous of me to blame him but I can't stand the strain of being the "good little wife" when in fact I want him dead so that I can get on with my life. No I don't have a lover waiting to marry me if that's what you're thinking. What's more I feel very very sorry for him. No-one deserves to die so young. What's getting me is being such a hypocrite, making people feel I love him when in fact I'm only doing what anyone would do in such a situation. Now I want to get on with my life, God forgive me.'

What about the third who remain together but are not exactly happy love birds? We see them in hospices too, of course, usually as characters in real-life bedroom farces as good as any produced in the West End. What usually happens is that a nurse is tipped off by a patient that he hopes to have a lady visitor and is worried by the possibility that she may arrive at the same time that his wife is visiting. He asks if there is anything we can do to save his embarrassment (though I have always thought it must be just as embarrassing for the two ladies concerned). On more occasions than I could count the staff were to be found shepherding one out of the ward by one door as the other was being escorted up the corridor by another nurse. When she had sat down comfortably by his chair or bedside the signal was given that the first one, whether wife or 'friend', could be allowed to slip out hopefully unnoticed by her competitor in the love stakes.

How often I have walked past the Reception Desk where our ever-welcoming receptionist was speaking to a lady visitor and explaining that she would have to check that the nurses had finished whatever it was they were doing for her husband before she let her in. She might then turn to me and ask 'Doctor, do you know if there is anyone in with Mr X?' We both knew what she was really asking.

Of course, life is never straightforward as we all know. There was one quite famous patient who asked us to be helpful and discrete about his two lady visitors, one his wife and the other his friend of many years. What he never learnt was that when he was admitted for what both he and his visitors understood would be the last time, the two ladies visited separately but were to be seen leaving together. Apparently they had known each other for many years, the wife had long known that the other one was her husband's mistress but they remained good friends, and now to cap it all, the mistress was staying with the wife to make their sad visiting easier. How well I remember the day he died. I walked to the door with them and asked what they were going to do. 'Open a bottle of champagne, of course, in memory of a very special man.' I could not help thinking that he may well have been a very special man but he had had two very special ladies in his life.

How is it that we all deceive ourselves into thinking we know everything there is to know about our husbands or wives? We have seen the protective husband who knows that if his wife finds he has cancer 'it will be the death of her' but what a strain it must be for men or women who have 'friends' and come to the end of their lives convinced their partner knows nothing about the affair. Each person in that *ménage à trois* must want to show their love but cannot; each must want to talk openly but cannot; and so a life ends not so much a dignified drama but more a charade.

Not all relationships were secret, as we soon discovered. One of the saddest ladies I ever saw was one who visited a gentleman accompanied by her husband. The two men obviously got along well together but it was only just before our patient died that we found that he was a lodger in their home and had been the lady's lover for many years, a state of affairs apparently well known to her husband. Once again I was fascinated that a man could be so caring and understanding as he comforted his wife after the death of her lodger-lover.

We have mentioned already how quickly patients make friends with other patients, often from very different walks of life and with vastly different interests and hobbies and backgrounds. Interestingly the same applies to visiting relatives. In no time you saw one bringing in another in their car or waiting to accompany someone to the bus stop. It is often said that Death is a great leveller. I suggest we might equally well speak of Grief as a leveller. Our social differences, even our religious barriers, are soon forgotten when we find so much in common in our grief. Why, oh why, do we have to get to that point in life to learn that?

Children, as all children do, soon get together to play in the special adventure playground provided for them or in the little ones' creche. Teenagers, of course, did their own thing, as always. Not for them any playing with children when they could be sitting around reading magazines or even watching 'telly' with a can of Coke in their hands, trying to look as though life was going on as normal when, as we all knew, it was falling apart. Looking back, what a lot of mistakes we must have made with those youngsters.

A few weeks after a young dad died in the hospice his teenage son phoned me of his own accord. I was both delighted to hear from him and somewhat put out by his tone of voice. 'If I come in will you have a can of Coke with me and I can tell you why I hate you?' It was difficult to sound excited about the invitation especially as I was not fond of Coke and had never enjoyed being told why someone hated me. We fixed a time. Perhaps Coke had a tranquillizing effect on me because it all turned out to be much less upsetting than I had expected.

'Good to see you again but you said something about hating me. What was that all about?'

'Well maybe I don't really hate you but I'm mad with you because you told me a lie about my Dad,' he began. 'That time I met you and asked how bad he was you said he would never get better, remember? When I asked if he would get stronger and maybe walk again you said no, he wouldn't. When I asked if he would ever come home to Mum and me you said no. Remember?'

'I remember all that very well and am really sorry about it but why are you mad with me?'

'You never said he was going to die! When you said he wouldn't get better I thought you meant he'd always be here in this hospital. That's why I hate you. You didn't have the courage to tell me the real truth.'

This was a lesson to me, one I should have learned many years before. Young people do not want euphemisms such as 'very ill indeed' or 'not likely to get better'. They want what they would call 'the truth – Dad is so ill that he will die.' I told him how sorry I was to have failed him when he most needed my help and friendship and he seemed happier now that he had got everything off his chest. In fact I am sure he forgave me, or was it revenge? He offered to buy me another Coke with his spending money!

What an obvious thing to say, but how often we forget. Children are children, not small adults! To children the world is black or white as most of us have found out as trainee parents. We seem to pay so little attention to their grief wrapped up as we are in our own. Simon was an eleven-year-old whose dad died in our care. He lost not only a dad but an idol and his best pal, I think. He too phoned me once and asked if I would be in the hospice one weekend because he had something he wanted to show me. His mum came on the line, full of apologies and explanations, because she felt this was such an imposition on me, though clearly she too rather hoped I would see him. I looked forward to it.

He walked in carrying a model plane he had just completed. 'Does it fly?' I enquired.

'Come outside on to the lawn and I'll show you! You're just like my dad, doubting if I can make a plane that'll fly.' He was right. It flew perfectly. No wonder he was proud. I told him of models I had made that were supposed to fly but crashed every time and how much I really admired what he had made.

'You see, doctor, my dad said I couldn't do it so I thought that if I showed you it would be a bit like showing Dad if you see what I mean. Now the next thing I'm going to do I'll have to do with just Mum there. Sorry you can't come.' I asked him what that was.

'We're going to where Dad is buried so that I can sort of tell him that I've been selected for the school first eleven soccer team. He always said he'd be proud if I made it.' He had every reason to be a proud Dad.

Enough of these sad and poignant stories, for the time being at least. What about the really happy memories, those memorable dinners for two! Every now and then the nurses would discover that it was someone's special wedding anniversary, say a silver or a gold. Perhaps a couple had fallen back in love after some time at a distance from each other, one of those amazing reconciliations we see in this work. They would then organize a candle-lit dinner for two in a little room, flowers on the table, something very special on the menu and a bottle of whatever wine the patient might still be able to enjoy. In the background whatever music they loved, wrapping them in memories. It was not difficult to organize and was certainly not expensive to provide, particularly if the wine had been donated, but the benefits simply could not be counted.

Happiness is such an infectious thing, isn't it? Why did we never hear about that in medical school? In spite of all the sadness and seriousness there are always funny things happening in hospices as there are in hospitals so let me a few stories of unintentional humour.

Let us start with the old lady whose deaf old husband was having considerable trouble passing water, a not uncommon problem for us men. We explained to her that we would need to pass a little rubber tube up his 'water pipe' into the bladder but, as she had become accustomed to doing, she decided to tell him herself, shouting so that not only he but everyone else within a mile radius could hear. 'They're going to put a cataract up your whatnot.' Readers will, I feel sure, realize that the word she meant was not cataract but catheter. Being a lady I feel sure she *did* mean 'whatnot'.

A nurse standing near by thought she should help her and save her further embarrassment. She explained that the thing that would be put into her husband's water pipe was a catheter, not a cataract. The old lady was too agitated to hear properly so proceeded to shout to him that she had got it wrong. 'You're going to have a cataract taken *out* of your water pipe.' At this point the nurse left, either because she was laughing so much or because she realized how helpful all the laughter was.

The following day, desperate to see what it (the catheter that is) looked like, she was the first visitor into the ward. She walked up to his bed, never said a word to him but lifted the bedclothes and stared at the centre of attention, exclaiming in a voice no-one could fail to hear 'not very big is it?' The comments of his fellow patients are not printable.

Bodily functions form the basis for many jokes but none better than the lady who had grown accustomed to hearing from her husband of his constipation which everything except dynamite had failed to move. Visiting time found relatives and friends round the other three beds in his room as he watched for her arrival at the door. It was unlikely he would fail to see her for she was the size and shape of a refrigerator. She pushed open the door, stood there, more than adequately filling the space and shouted 'Have they moved yet?' to which everyone else in the room replied in chorus 'No!'

I have always been a believer that a doctor should be on the same eye level as the person he is speaking to, preferably sitting beside them rather than on the other side of the table, and only when it is not likely to offend, touching them. I did that one day with a lady whose mother had just come in. Totally innocently I put a hand on her knee only to hear her say 'You won't get far with that one, doctor. That's my artificial leg,' to the amusement of her husband and everyone else who was there.

Just occasionally there is a joke at the expense of a patient, but not an unkind one because it is made by a caring, loving family, in this case one which had far deeper insights than we professionals had.

I once looked after a lady who appeared to be comfortable, not only to me but to the nurses – a far more demanding and critical group than the doctors – but who day in, day out, told us she was never free from pain. None of our treatment had been effective, she said, and she must now resign herself to dying in agony of body and mind. We spent hours and hours with her, looking into her physical pain, her fears, her regrets, her beliefs – everything which might be contributing to such a terrible state of affairs. One of the most junior nurses mentioned that she slept and ate remarkably well for someone in pain and wondered if it was physical pain or just the way she described everything. I decided to meet her family, explain our dilemma to them, apologize that I and the team had failed and then offer to have her transferred to wherever they wanted her to be for the type of care she needed and deserved. Such humility does not come naturally to some of us!

About eight of them sat in a circle, some on chairs, some on the arms of chairs, the youngest on the floor as I gave my carefully prepared presentation. I shall never know what they expected but their faces were tense with worry. I must have looked as uncomfortable myself. I hoped for an understanding response rather than harsh criticism but had never bargained for laughter. They were very amused and said so.

When I had finished one of the daughters spoke up. 'Doctor, was that all you wanted to tell us?' I nodded. Another daughter spoke, looking round to make sure everyone was nodding agreement. 'As for the pain, well she's told us she's in agony as far back as any of us can remember. I was never allowed to bring any friends home from school because Mum always had a headache.'

'Come on. It was worse than that for me. Don't you remember that Mum wasn't sure if she'd get to my wedding because she had such a headache,' said another. 'Of course she did come and was the life and soul of the party after a few drinks.'

'Mum and her headaches. We learned to live with them, doctor,' said another. 'They never stopped her going out to the Bingo and even when she won something she still said she had a headache. Dad used to think he was the only one who had to live with her headaches, didn't you, Dad.' Roars of laughter.

'There's plenty of us,' said one of the daughters, 'so she can't have had headaches every night, Dad!' Even more laughter.

'We were wanting to meet you before you invited us here today, because we wanted to tell you and everyone here that we've never seen Mum so happy and content. We all think you've done a great job with her, don't we?' and she turned to the others for their enthusiastic agreement.

They were a united and loving family, for all their shrewd insights into Mum's behaviour, and would have been the first to tell us if we could do more to help her. That little vignette does, however, remind us that people develop their own coping strategies and behaviour patterns and often continue to employ them to the end.

Perhaps that sounds like an uncharitable criticism of a lady coming to the end of life, as if we are laughing at her expense.

Certainly not. We are reminding ourselves that families have deep insights which can help the professional carers; that they can often be remarkably objective though less so when looking at pain, and that everyone has their own defence mechanism, their manipulative technique honed over the years.

However, even here there are lessons for us. One thing that never ceased to surprise, and I must also say disappoint, me was how apprehensive people are about looking after their loved one when the are critically ill. We have just looked at the gentleman who was doing so well at home but the family asked for him to be admitted and, without a shadow of doubt, it was for their sake and not his. Perhaps I have chosen the wrong word when I say they were apprehensive for surely that is more than justified.

Better words which come to mind are terrified, reluctant, astonished at being asked to care for them or being expected to do so. Time after time I have heard otherwise deeply caring people say, 'I can't do it – you see I'm not trained to do it.' Or, meaning the same thing 'I'm not qualified.' Are they seriously saying that you have to have gone through some formal educational or training programme before you can look after someone you love? Bizarre as it sounds, I believe that is indeed what they are saying. Can you imagine it – 'I took Care of the Dying in my GCSE'?

Perhaps the reasons for this are not difficult to find. Few people now die at home, in stark contrast to the situation at the beginning of the 20th Century, with the result that fewer and fewer people have experience of caring for the seriously ill there, or even of seeing what such an illness looks like. Little over 50 years ago only about thirty percent of people died in hospital, the rest being cared for at home. Today in Britain less than thirty percent die at home in spite of the excellence of general practitioners and their nurse colleagues, and the existence of literally hundreds of Macmillan nurses and hospice Home Care Services. The number of professionals and the abundance of skilled expertise and support

available to help care for people at home has never been greater –
yet still the trend continues to keep them at home for a while then
have them admitted to a hospital for 'terminal care'. Yes, to a
hospital for, perhaps surprisingly, only a very small percentage ever
see the inside of a hospice or palliative care unit.

That may be the first reason – we have got out of the way of
caring for people at home and society no longer expects it. At times
it looks to me as though society no longer tolerates it. It must be
asked, though, what brought about this change. Is this a reflection
of another feature of our modern society – the belief that it takes
experts to do a thing well and, as we all know, you can only be
expert if you have undertaken advanced training? If this is so, and
I suspect it is, then making palliative care a specialty may have
made the situation worse. Rather than seeing Macmillan nurses
and palliative medicine consultant specialists for what they are –
experts to be called in when extra support or specialist skills might
help in what is perceived as a very difficult situation – people may
suspect that only people with their training and years and years of
experience can do such caring. 'How can I be expected to care for
Mum dying of advanced cancer when some doctors and nurses
have to train for an additional four years or more to do this work?'
seems to be what many people are saying. I find this very sad though
I think I understand what they are feeling.

I feel sadder still when I see how embarrassed and ill-at-ease so
many people are when they visit their loved ones in hospital or
hospice, and now we are not speaking of 'the lady and the catheter'
or any of the others we have smiled at. Rather am I remembering
the hundreds, no the thousands, I have watched as they have sat
beside patients under my care. Most seem not to have any idea
what to talk about or even how to relax together and enjoy this
precious time. Do any ever come prepared, I often wondered? How
many people buy little notebooks in which to write the questions
raised by the patient and, at the other end, little bits of news to tell
the patient? Very, very few. Instead they come in, puffing and

panting after what has often been a long and tiring journey, and immediately start talking about his illness or his bowels, problems which he is probably trying to put at the back of his mind for the next few hours, if he is allowed to.

They are even more uncomfortable and 'helpless' when the end is near, either crowding in around the patient like a disorderly rugby scrum, sometimes two deep as they peer down over him, or sitting several feet away, motionless and silent and expressionless, not even daring to hold his hand or whisper 'sweet nothings' in his ear.

I suppose it must have happened and I have forgotten but I cannot recall ever being asked by a relative if they could help feed their loved one, or help clean her mouth or give a drink, or help prop them up in bed, guided if needs be by a nurse. Many many times have we nurses and doctors suggested they do so and, as you would expect, they have done it superbly well, with a gentleness and a compassion which even the 'trained' might not be able to better.

Does any of this matter? I believe profoundly that it does. If, for whatever reason, terminally ill people are to spend their final weeks and days away from home, then surely they deserve to be helped to feel as 'at home' as it is possible to do. Hospitals are terrifying places at the best of times, every sound, every smell, every part of the day's routine being different from home, sometimes even your name ignored by staff, all of whom both are and look to be overworked and stressed out. Places of hope and healing they may be but there can be few places which more speedily and efficiently depersonalize those who enter them. Hospices set out to be better than hospitals and I believe that most are but, and it is a large but, they are inextricably associated with suffering, pain, loneliness and death. I do not care how warm the welcome, how skilfully selected the staff, how carefully chosen the fabric and the furniture, it is not home.

Let me be the medical heretic once again even if it means facing the Inquisition. I would rather that we did all in our power to enable people to be cared for at home until their death, even if the care was perhaps less expert than they might get in the nearest hospice or palliative care unit, than that they should end their days in a place where they were ill-at-ease and their relatives looked and acted as if they were too scared to breathe.

Perhaps one final anecdote will say it all better than I can hope to do.

I waited until a gentleman had said goodbye to his wife after she had sat with him most of the day. He sat on the edge of his bed, gave her a kiss and watched as she went to the door, turned round and waved to him, then went for her bus. Then I went to him to say something but before I could do so he muttered 'Poor soul! She always looks so frightened and lonely. You would think it was her who was going to die, not me. If we were at home I'd just take her into my arms and give her a hug or maybe we'd cuddle up to each other in front of the fire. Of course, if I was at home she probably wouldn't be as scared as she is in here.'

Chapter XII

Au Revoir

'Attending and accompanying with the patient in his dying is, in fact, the oldest medical ethic there is.'   Paul Ramsey

Well, this book has certainly demonstrated the dangers of speaking to a fellow traveller on a long journey, particularly if the man in the seat beside you is a garrulous doctor. All you asked was what his business was and then expressed interest in hospices where he had worked. You never bargained for this, but at least it saved you watching the in-flight film!

Perhaps the reader has realized it already but the book has not really been about hospices *per se* but about the care they offer, the people they serve and the lessons we are all learning from being with those people and their loved ones. If there is one impression that the reader must not go away with, and which the author never intended to give, it is that hospices, and those who work in them, are unique. Nothing could be farther from the truth. They have no monopoly on love and care. The same concern and compassion can be found in most hospitals around the world. The staff are neither more caring nor more dedicated than many of their colleagues in most hospitals and nursing homes. The difference is in their focus and in the rewards. Whether they like it or not, general hospitals focus on *curing*. They undoubtedly care for their patients, often exceedingly skilfully and sensitively, but almost all their efforts are directed towards cure, or keeping their patients alive as long as possible. They simply do not have sufficient beds to admit people for long stays and the pressures of the work are such that, even when staff want to spend longer with their patients, they simply do not have the time or the opportunity to do so.

Hospices, or palliative care units as we now realize we should call them, are unashamedly for people who will die within a few months. Much as professionals such as the author and his colleagues might wish that their illness could be cured they recognize the futility of 'cure medicine' for them. Equally they recognize and accept the undeniable imperative that all suffering must be relieved. That, in a nutshell, is hospice or palliative care, something which can and should be available whether the person is being cared for in their own home, or in a hospital or nursing home, or in a special place set apart for them. As has been remarked by many observers, there is little new in this caring ministry we call hospice care. It is not new but rather a re-discovery, a re-affirmation of an integral part of all good care. Long, long before there were such things as hospices and palliative care services, good doctors and nurses sought to ease pain and suffering as part of their daily work. The difference was that they did not give this component of their work a fancy name as we do now, and to be fair, they did not have at their disposal all the expertise and knowledge we have today, enough to merit palliative care being listed as a specialty.

The focus is different and so too are the rewards. We have all known the thrill and the delight in seeing someone leave a hospital almost unrecognizable from the person who came in a week or two before. A difficult diagnosis had been made or a complicated operation performed and as a result health has been restored. Those were heady days, but the rewards in palliative care are every bit as exciting and moving. The rewards lie not just in seeing agony relieved and breathing made easier but in the amazing trust people place in their carers. What greater excitement can there be than being asked to share in someone's final journey?

It is this highly focused care which has brought us the insights described in this book. Patients somehow felt liberated to speak as they had never done before, sharing experiences and feelings so buried, so intimate that few had suspected they existed. As very ill people often do, whatever their illness, our patients showed such trust in us, the professional carers, that we too felt safe to look into our inner selves and discover things we never knew existed. Most of us went into this work because we knew that the quality of our caring could be improved, and that our students could be better trained and inspired. We somehow knew without being told that our patients deserved as good care as death approached as we had tried to give them throughout their lives. What most of us had never anticipated was that we would learn so much and feel so profoundly humbled by this experience.

Understandably the author, now retired from clinical work, is often asked what, if anything, he misses from his 'active' days. The list is endless. There is the indescribable thrill of seeing someone admitted with searing pain sitting up in bed only a day or so later, free of pain for the first time in weeks. There is the family reunited after years of separation and bickering; or the lonely old man without a friend in the world who finds friendship and happiness in the hospice. There is the unforgettable sight of children sitting round their daddy's bedside and asking why he has to die or the young widow coming back with her children to spend the first anniversary of his death in the hospice because it felt the safest place to be that day.

Life being what it is, not all memories are happy ones. We must not romanticize the hospice any more than we must not sanitize death. The mind goes back to those times of tension familiar to all doctors, and as common in a hospice as anywhere else, where there were more people needing to be admitted than there were beds for, to the angry relatives who blamed anybody and everybody but never themselves, and to the personality conflicts which seem to afflict all human endeavour. There are times in a hospice when it feels like a battleground, not a haven of peace. The challenge was to make it feel like peace for the patients even when it was a battleground for the rest of us. To make them feel we had all the time in the world when, in fact, we wondered how we would ever fit into 24 hours the work that had to be done. Sometimes we failed! One man, seeing me dashing around when I should have been creating that serenity we have spoken of, asked me as I passed his bed 'Did the Good Lord put too few hours into each day, doctor?'

However, none of these are the first to come to mind when the question is asked 'What do you most miss?' The greatest 'miss' is that 'high' (if you will pardon the Americanism) which came from just being with people in their hour of greatest need, seeing how they coped and how they seemed to grow before our eyes. The shy and retiring found sufficient confidence even to assist others, whilst the terrified found courage beyond imagining; those without faith often found it and those who had forgotten how to love were to be seen befriending someone even worse off than themselves. What that does to those who stand and watch is almost impossible to describe.

You become aware of a basic human goodness you had long thought lost from our materialistic and cynical society. You find yourself speaking of love and doing so without embarrassment, realizing that even if it cannot be measured and its effect evaluated (as modern evidence-based medicine demands), it is nevertheless a power to be reckoned with. It is not fashionable to speak like this today. We have grown suspicious of such talk. Love has become synonymous with sex and its portrayal by the media, not as we see it in hospice care where it is so generous, unselfish and undemanding. We have become cynical about human nature, unable to accept that people *can* act without ulterior motives, that they can be genuinely sincere, and can be trusted.

In an age when public image and the impressions we create are given such high priority it is incredibly refreshing to work with people for whom these things have no importance whatsoever. I remember as if it was yesterday a gentleman being visited by his wife. He had suggested doing something, I cannot recall what, and she was concerned about what people might say. 'Darling, I am now at a point in my life when people must accept me for who I am and what I have done. I have stopped adding to my *curriculum vitae*.' To work with people who no longer have to pretend to be what they are not, no longer have to feign feelings, is so refreshing. Looking back on our lives, is it not true that most of us spend an inordinate amount of time pretending to be what we are not. We feign courage when we are terrified, fascination when we are bored, insights when we are baffled, and affection when we do not feel it. 'I think I only discovered my real self when I came in here,' said one man. 'It was quite a revelation.'

But another thing one misses is the constant learning, those daily surprises which were so exciting. Who would ever have thought that so many terminally ill people not only know what is the matter with them but some of them even know when they are going to die? At some time or other we all realize that our body language is saying something about how we are feeling or even about our personality but I suspect few doctors realize how skilled their patients are at interpreting that body language. 'I just knew from the way he stood there, keeping his distance from me, that he had bad news and didn't know how to tell me. I said to myself "Poor man! He's scared and he doesn't want me or anyone else to know."'

Most doctors and nurses will say that they wish they had more time to devote to their dying patients but time is a very scarce commodity in their daily lives. They imagine, as indeed I did before doing this work, that dying patients will want to talk and talk on every subject under the sun; going over and over every detail of their illness; reliving much of their lives and pouring out their feelings and their fears. It simply does not happen. The nearer a person comes to the end of life the greater their appreciation of how precious is time, particularly the time of their carers. 'Your time is very precious, doctor. What matters is that I know you'll give me a few minutes when I really need it.'

This is, I suggest, more important than might at first appear.

One of the commonest reasons given for not giving the best care to the dying is that there simply is not sufficient time to do so, much as the caring doctor or nurse wants to. Experience shows, beyond any possible doubt, that people coming to the end of life want 'quality' time rather than a long time. Even five minutes sitting on their bed may be all they want if you are ready to listen or prepared to answer their questions honestly and simply. What they do not want is a one-sided conversation devoid of substance or, worse still, one full of platitudes or patronizing. 'If I had wanted someone to come in and discuss the football scores I could easily have found one. I certainly didn't ask my minister to come in for that.'

Of course, one of the painful lessons we learned was that when someone says they would like those few minutes of your time they meant sooner rather than delayed until later. It was a sad experience to go back in an hour or so, after dealing with what you regarded as more urgent business, to be told that they no longer wanted to talk to you because 'it doesn't matter now, thank you.' The immediacy of their needs and their questions took most of us by surprise. Once again, we had not been prepared for this in our training. It was not that they were being unreasonable or demanding. It was simply that they had come to know the benefit of honest answers to their questions. The sooner they had those answers the sooner some of their fears would be dispelled.

Neither had anyone taught us that patients usually know how much information they can take in and digest at any one time. Yes, they want to know, indeed they have a right to be told, but most people have an in-built safety mechanism which warns them that they will experience information overload if they get any more facts. How obvious, you might say, but it is far from obvious to doctors. Too often we feel that if we have 'told them everything there is to tell about the condition' our patients are bound to feel better and, hopefully, very appreciative. Said a worldly-wise old man to me once after his doctor had given a long, textbook style description of his illness, 'If you ask me, doctor, I think he was just trying to show me how clever he was.'

It took years of hospice work to teach me that what patients want to know is not necessarily what the doctors assume they want or need to be told. It is not necessarily the diagnosis of a mortal illness which most frightens many people but the suffering that illness will bring. In fact it is not necessarily the suffering but the uncertainty whether or not doctors will be interested in that suffering and care enough to do something about it. One of the greatest tragedies of modern medicine, or so it seems to me, is not the amount of suffering we see but that so much of it is unnecessary when we have the weapons to deal with it if we choose to use them. I suppose another tragedy is how seldom we professional carers listen to what our patients want to tell us of that suffering. Too often we seem to assume that if they do not mention something there is nothing to mention; or we deceive ourselves into thinking that their worst problems must be their physical ones of pain or sickness or whatever else they have. In fact they are more distressed by the grief of the family or the uncertain future for their children, but like all well-trained professionals we focus on the things we have been taught to deal with, preferring to ignore those we find daunting or impossible.

That was another 'discovery' for the author. Put simply it is that the nearer someone comes to the end of their life the more considerate they are to others and the better they are to know and to be with. It reminds us of the cantankerous old man whose wife wondered what wonder drug we had put him on. As the end draws near they less and less mention their own suffering but talk more and more of those they are leaving behind and their concerns for them. They become not only more thoughtful and considerate but also, if we may use such a word of macho men as well as women, softer, more gentle. They are often less argumentative or abrasive, less quarrelsome or critical. In a word, they are good to be with. How often can we say that about the men and women we meet in our ordinary daily lives, I wonder? Is it any wonder so many of us in palliative care feel it is the most wonderful job in the world? We are truly privileged.

I am sure people will read this little book and say 'All very interesting but what has this got to do with me? I'm not dying so far as I know and, thank God, I'm not visiting a member of my family in a hospice somewhere.'

My answer would be that some of the lessons we have learnt seem as relevant to life outside a hospice as to life inside it, to those blessed with health as much as to those without health. The power of love is one example. Surely no-one would deny that our world seems to be full of conflict and cruelty, of jealousies and backbiting, with never a TV news programme without stories of corruption and crime. It feels as though we have to be more careful than ever before to protect our children, not only against complete strangers but even members of their families, that we have to teach them defensive living, inculcating in them a sense of suspicion bordering on cynicism. Life has become more competitive than ever before. A 'good' man, a 'successful' woman, is now someone who has made a fortune, not someone who has put others before themselves. So cynical have we become that we even look with suspicion on a person who works for nothing as a voluntary worker or who turns down the prospect of a lucrative job to spend more time with his family. He must have an ulterior motive or be making something on the side!

The message from our hospice patients was 'thank you for accepting me, in spite of who I am, what I have done, how ugly this cancer has made me and how peculiar I may be.' As one nurse said to a patient in my hearing 'Here we love you and look after you just because you are you.' Unconditional love, with no strings attached.

If more of us lived like that or followed that ethic, would the world be a better place? If more families knew how rewarding it can be to look after a dying loved one would they try to do so or can we expect that from now we shall just hear 'I can't do it – I'm not trained, you see'?

What does it take to do this caring? I ask that question fully aware that it must be very different being a relative from being a professional carer. At the end of each day I and my colleagues could go home, home to a different world of children, crises, laughter and love, a world where we could put many of the events of the day behind us. The relative does not have that luxury, that refreshment but must carry their caring burden in spite of exhaustion and grief, and often in the face of criticism and minimal assistance from other relatives. Nevertheless I am asking the question because it strikes me as odd and almost a little sinister that as each year passes fewer and fewer people die in their own beds, their simple needs met by their loved ones.

Is Death the final taboo as has so often been suggested? How is it that we seem ready to look after our loved ones at home, often with illnesses that only a few decades ago would have necessitated hospital admissions, but when it comes to the *final* stages of a fatal illness we lose our resolve? Do we really feel inadequate, as is often said, or do we not like to be reminded of our own mortality? I recall a young man telling me how frightened he felt sitting at the bedside of his partner dying of AIDS, knowing full well that what he was watching would be his fate in the not-too-distant future.

If it is our mortality which frightens us then I have no answer. That must say something about the diminishing place of religion in our society as well about our material lives probably being better than we care to admit. Perhaps they are so good that we seldom address those existential questions until near the end, as our patients so often did. Why think about tomorrow when today is good? I have no answer but I have my fears. What kind of society have we become when we cannot face mortality, an unavoidable, undeniable feature of human life?

If we are troubled by our sense of inadequacy for this caring role then certainly our patients have much to teach us, whether we are highly trained professionals or 'ordinary' people. Better than most of us ever thought possible, they know when they need medical skills and when they need companionship. Much as it might surprise a doctor to learn it, there are times when his professional qualifications are not as important to a patient as his willingness to be a friend rather than a physician. Should he protest that time does not allow of such a luxury for him or his patient, he will then find that dying people have the most acute appreciation of time. They never waste it. However much time they may have wasted in the past they value every minute when their time is short, and are equally aware of how busy their carers are.

Being a friend rather than a health care professional is not as easy as it sounds. You cannot hide beneath your professional facade, nor baffle the patient with your jargon. You have to be prepared to listen rather than to talk and there's the rub. Most people are not good listeners, and doctors and nurses are no exception. Our patients taught us that we have to do more than hear them – we have to *listen*, and that demands concentration, interest, and commitment.

It soon dawns on us that being wanted as friends rather than as professionals is an enormous honour. They are telling us that they know the difference between our professional skills and knowledge and our virtues as friends; that they have learned when they want one and not the other. Friends are people who accept you without question, people who care and want little in return, people who can bear to see you cry and can laugh and cry with you. Friends are people who are happy to purchase platform tickets.

What do I miss, you asked? I miss sitting beside people waiting for their train to come in, all packed and ready to go to that place they have heard so much about yet never seen, the 'undiscovered country from whose bourn no traveller returns' as Shakespeare describes it. Sitting beside them as a friend more than as a doctor yet still respected and appreciated for my professional skills. Sitting beside them at the start of the loneliest and probably the shortest journey we all must go on, not needing to speak, not needing to impress, just sharing humanity. What an honour to be asked to get that platform ticket. It makes you think even more of packing a bag and sitting there with that single ticket, doesn't it?

'Come my friends. 'Tis not too late to seek a better world'
Tennyson